Target
Get back on track 5

Edexcel GCSE (9–1)
English Literature

Macbeth

David Grant

Pearson

Published by Pearson Education Limited, 80 Strand, London, WC2R 0RL.

www.pearsonschoolsandfecolleges.co.uk

Copies of official specifications for all Pearson qualifications may be found on the website: qualifications.pearson.com

Text © Pearson Education Ltd 2017
Typeset by Tech-Set Ltd, Gateshead

The right of David Grant to be identified as author of this work has been asserted by him in accordance with the Copyright, Designs and Patents Act 1988.

First published 2017

ARP impression 98

British Library Cataloguing in Publication Data
A catalogue record for this book is available from the British Library

ISBN 978 1 292 23009 2

Printed in Great Britain by Ashford Colour Press Ltd

Notes from the publisher
Pearson has robust editorial processes, including answer and fact checks, to ensure the accuracy of the content in this publication, and every effort is made to ensure this publication is free of errors. We are, however, only human, and occasionally errors do occur. Pearson is not liable for any misunderstandings that arise as a result of errors in this publication, but it is our priority to ensure that the content is accurate. If you spot an error, please do contact us at resourcescorrections@pearson.com so we can make sure it is corrected.

Contents

① Getting the plot straight

This unit will help you to understand and remember the plot of *Macbeth*. The skills you will build are to:

* remember the sequence of key events in the play
* understand the causes and consequences of the key events in the play
* understand what makes some events in the play more significant than others.

In the exam you will face questions like the one below. This is about the extract on the next page. At the end of the unit you will **plan your own response** to the **second part** of this question.

Exam-style question

a Explore how Shakespeare presents the character of Macbeth in this extract.
  Refer closely to the extract in your answer.   **(20 marks)**

b This extract shows the influence of the supernatural on the characters of Macbeth and Banquo.

  Explain the importance of the supernatural elsewhere in the play.

  In your answer you must consider:
  * how the supernatural is shown
  * the impact of the supernatural on the play's action and characters.

  You should refer to the context of the play in your answer.   **(20 marks)**

Before you tackle the question you will work through three key questions in the **skills boosts** to help you to get the plot of *Macbeth* straight.

 How do I make sure I know the plot?

 How can I explore the development of the plot?

 How do I know which are the most significant events in the play?

Read the extract on the next page from Act 1 Scene 3 of *Macbeth*.

As you read, think about the following: ✓

Where in the play does this scene appear? Is it near the beginning, in the middle or at the end?

What has happened before this scene? What happens after this scene?

Why is the supernatural so important in this scene?

Exam-style question

In this extract, Macbeth and Banquo have a conversation, after the witches have told Macbeth that he will become Thane of Cawdor and King of Scotland.

Extract A | Act 1 Scene 3 of *Macbeth*

MACBETH
Stay, you imperfect speakers, tell me more:
By Sinel's death I know I am Thane of Glamis;
But how of Cawdor? The Thane of Cawdor lives,
A prosperous gentleman; and to be king
5   Stands not within the prospect of belief,
No more than to be Cawdor. Say from whence
You owe this strange intelligence, or why
Upon this blasted heath you stop our way
With such prophetic greeting? Speak, I charge you.
Witches vanish
BANQUO
10 The earth hath bubbles, as the water has,
And these are of them. Whither are they vanish'd?
MACBETH
Into the air; and what seem'd corporal melted
As breath into the wind. Would they had stay'd!
BANQUO
Were such things here as we do speak about?
15 Or have we eaten on the insane root
That takes the reason prisoner?
MACBETH
Your children shall be kings.
BANQUO
You shall be king.
MACBETH
And Thane of Cawdor too: went it not so?

How do I make sure I know the plot?

One way to make sure you know the plot of *Macbeth* is to focus on some of the more memorable, key events that happen in the play.

Look at this list of characters in the play. Use it to help you answer the questions below.

Macbeth	**Duncan**, King of Scotland	**Lennox**, nobleman
Lady Macbeth	**Malcolm**, elder son of Duncan	**Ross**, nobleman
Seyton, Macbeth's servant	**Donalbain**, younger son of Duncan	**Menteith**, nobleman
	Duncan's guards	**Angus**, nobleman
Banquo, a general		**Caithness**, nobleman
Fleance, his son	**Hecate**, queen of the witches	
	The three witches	**Siward**, Earl of Northumberland
Macduff, Thane of Fife		**Young Siward**, his son
Lady Macduff, his wife		
Boy, son of Macduff		**Three murderers**

1. Several characters die in the play. Cross out all the characters in the list above who die during the play.

2. How many times does Macbeth meet the witches in the play? Circle Ⓐ the correct answer.

once		twice		three times

3. a. What is the first thing that happens in the play? Write ✏ your answer in box 1 of the plot summary below.

   b. What happens at the end of the play? Write ✏ your answer in box 12 below.

   c. Add ✏ Macbeth's meetings with the witches and all the deaths in the play to the plot summary below. Aim to get each meeting and each death in the correct order. You might not fill every box.

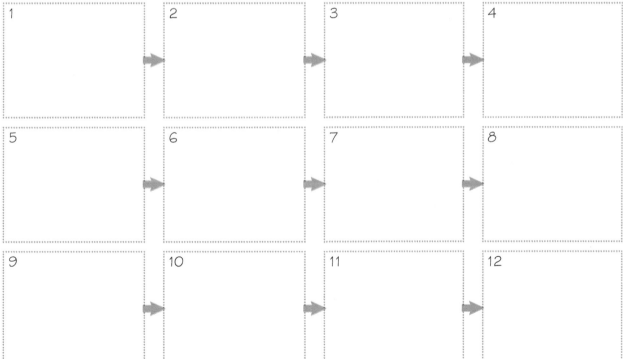

How can I explore the development of the plot?

Understanding the causes and consequences of key events in *Macbeth* will help you to get the plot straight and to understand how the plot develops.

Look at some of the key events in *Macbeth*.

Causes   Consequences

> 1.2 Macbeth fights bravely to repel the invading Norwegian army.

> 1.3 Macbeth and Banquo hear the witches' predictions: Macbeth will become Thane of Cawdor and King of Scotland.

> 1.4 Macbeth is made Thane of Cawdor.

> 1.5–1.7 Lady Macbeth persuades Macbeth to kill King Duncan.

> 2.2 Macbeth murders King Duncan.

> 2.4 Macbeth is King of Scotland.

> 3.3 Macbeth has Banquo murdered.

> 3.4 Macbeth sees Banquo's ghost at the feast to celebrate his coronation.

> 4.1 The witches reveal that 'no man born of woman shall harm Macbeth' and that he should 'Beware Macduff'.

> 4.2 Macbeth has Macduff's wife and children murdered.

> 5.1 Lady Macbeth's mind is troubled by her husband's actions.

> 5.5 Lady Macbeth dies.

> 5.8 Macduff kills Macbeth. Malcolm is made King of Scotland.

(1) One of the key events in the play is the **murder of King Duncan**.

    a On the left of the list above, draw arrows (↓) to show the chain of **causes** that leads to Macbeth **murdering King Duncan**.

    b On the right-hand side, draw arrows (↓) to show the chain of **consequences** caused by the **murder of King Duncan**.

> One arrow for **cause** and one arrow for **consequence** have already been drawn for you to start the chain.

(2) Choose another significant event in the play and underline (A) it. Using a different colour, draw arrows (↓) on the left-hand side to show the chain of events that **causes** it, and on the right-hand side to show the chain of **consequences** that follows it.

3 How do I know which are the most significant events in the play?

Understanding how each key event contributes to the play will help you to get the plot straight and identify significant parts of the play to write about in your responses.

Look at some of the key events in *Macbeth*.

	✎	✓
1.2 Macbeth fights bravely to repel the invading Norwegian army.		
1.3 Macbeth and Banquo hear the witches' predictions: Macbeth will become Thane of Cawdor and King of Scotland.		
1.4 Macbeth is made Thane of Cawdor.		
1.5–1.7 Lady Macbeth persuades Macbeth to kill King Duncan.		
2.2 Macbeth murders King Duncan.		
2.4 Macbeth is King of Scotland.		
3.3 Macbeth has Banquo murdered.		
3.4 Macbeth sees Banquo's ghost at the feast to celebrate his coronation.		
4.1 The witches reveal that 'no man born of woman shall harm Macbeth' and that he should 'Beware Macduff'.		
4.2 Macbeth has Macduff's wife and children murdered.		
5.1 Lady Macbeth's mind is troubled by her husband's actions.		
5.5 Lady Macbeth dies.		
5.8 Macduff kills Macbeth. Malcolm is made King of Scotland.		

(1) How would the story of *Macbeth* change if Shakespeare had decided to cut all the scenes featuring the witches? Write ✎ **one** or **two** sentences explaining how the story would change.

....

....

....

(2) Now, think carefully about each of the key events listed above. For each one, ask yourself:

(?) How would the plot be altered if it was removed?   (?) How significant is it to the plot?

a Beside each key event, write ✎ a mark out of 10: give it 1 out of 10 if it is not at all significant, 5 out of 10 if it is quite significant, and 10 out of 10 if it is very significant.

b Tick ✓ the **three** events that you have given the highest mark. Annotate ✎ each one, explaining why you have decided it is so significant.

Get the plot straight

To write an effective response about *Macbeth*, you need to:

- know the key events in the play and the order in which they happen
- understand the causes and consequences of the key events in the play
- be able to identify the most significant events in the play and explain what makes them so significant.

Look again at the **first** part of the exam-style question you saw at the start of the unit.

Exam-style question

a Explore how Shakespeare presents the character of Macbeth in this extract.

Refer closely to the extract in your answer.

(20 marks)

Now look at one student's planning notes, written in response to this exam-style question.

> <u>Before this scene:</u> Macbeth is described as 'brave' by the Captain reporting the battle – 'well he deserves that name'.
>
> <u>After this scene:</u> Macbeth is plotting the murder of Duncan to make sure the witches' prediction comes true.
>
> Macbeth is transformed from hero to traitor by the witches' predictions. Could suggest that he is already ambitious and wants to believe he will be Thane of Cawdor and King – or perhaps shows his belief in the supernatural/ ability to predict the future, typical of beliefs in the 17th century.
>
> <u>In the extract:</u>
> He shows some doubt: 'to be king/Stands not within the prospect of belief'
> He clearly believes the witches - 'stay you imperfect speakers' - wants to hear more.
> He calls their news 'intelligence', suggesting he thinks it is fact.
> And neither Macbeth nor Banquo shows any doubt when they sum up the predictions: 'You (shall) be king.'

1. Think about all the ideas this student has included in their plan. Annotate 🖊 their plan, highlighting all the different elements that will make their response successful.

Your turn!

You are now going to **plan your own answer** in response to the **second part** of the exam-style question.

Exam-style question

b This extract shows the influence of the supernatural on the characters of Macbeth and Banquo. Explain the importance of the supernatural elsewhere in the play.

In your answer you must consider:
- how the supernatural is shown
- the impact of the supernatural on the play's action and characters.

You should refer to the context of the play in your answer.   **(20 marks)**

1 Look again at some of the key events in the play.   ✓

1.2 Macbeth fights bravely to repel the invading Norwegian army.	☐
1.3 Macbeth and Banquo hear the witches' predictions: Macbeth will become Thane of Cawdor and King of Scotland.	☐
1.4 Macbeth is made Thane of Cawdor.	☐
1.5–1.7 Lady Macbeth persuades Macbeth to kill King Duncan.	☐
2.2 Macbeth murders King Duncan.	☐
2.4 Macbeth is King of Scotland.	☐
3.3 Macbeth has Banquo murdered.	☐
3.4 Macbeth sees Banquo's ghost at the feast to celebrate his coronation.	☐
4.1 The witches reveal that 'no man born of woman shall harm Macbeth' and that he should 'Beware Macduff'.	☐
4.2 Macbeth has Macduff's wife and children murdered.	☐
5.1 Lady Macbeth's mind is troubled by her husband's actions.	☐
5.5 Lady Macbeth dies.	☐
5.8 Macduff kills Macbeth. Malcolm is made King of Scotland.	☐

a Which key events include elements of the supernatural? Tick ✓ them.

b Which of these elements of the supernatural have a significant impact on the play's action and characters? Tick ✓ them again.

c Which key events show the impact of the supernatural on the play's action and characters? List 🖉 them.

....

....

d Which are the most significant key events you would choose to write about in your response to the exam-style question above? Underline Ⓐ them.

Review your skills

Check up

Review your plan for the exam-style question on page 7. Tick ✓ the column to show how well you think you have done each of the following.

	Not quite ✓	Nearly there ✓	Got it! ✓
identified the key events in the play that include elements of the supernatural	☐	☐	☐
thought about key events in the play that show the influence of the supernatural on the play's action and characters	☐	☐	☐
selected the most significant events in the play showing the supernatural and its impact on the play's action and characters	☐	☐	☐

Look over all of your work in this unit. Note down 🖉 the **three** most important things to remember when planning your response to a *Macbeth* question.

1. ....

2. ....

3. ....

Need more practice?

Here is another exam-style question, this time relating to the extract from Act 1 Scene 2 on page 73 (Extract A).

Exam-style question

b This extract shows the violence of the battlefield.

Explain the importance of violence elsewhere in the play.

In your answer you must consider:

• how violence is shown

• the reasons for the violence.

You should refer to the context of the play in your answer. **(20 marks)**

Note down 🖉 the key events in the play you would choose to write about in your response to this question. You'll find some suggested ideas in the Answers section.

How confident do you feel about each of these **skills?** Colour 🖉 in the bars.

1 **How do I make sure I know the plot?**

2 **How can I explore the development of the plot?**

3 **How do I know which are the most significant events in the play?**

② Analysing the extract

This unit will help you to explore the extract in the *Macbeth* exam question. The skills you will build are to:

- select relevant points to make in your analysis
- develop your analysis
- structure your analysis.

In the exam you will face questions like the one below. This is about the extract on the next page. At the end of the unit you will **write one paragraph** in response to the **first part** of this question.

Exam-style question

a Explore how Shakespeare presents the character of Duncan as a leader in this extract.

Refer closely to the extract in your answer.   **(20 marks)**

b This extract shows Macbeth's desire for power.

Explain the importance of power and the desire for power elsewhere in the play.

In your answer you must consider:

- how power and the desire for power are shown
- the reasons that characters desire power and how power affects them.

You should refer to the context of the play in your answer.   **(20 marks)**

Before you tackle the question you will work through three key questions in the **skills boosts** to help you analyse the extract.

 How do I choose the points I need to make?   **How do I develop my analysis?**   **How do I structure a paragraph of analysis?**

Read the extract on the next page from Act 1 Scene 4 of *Macbeth*.

As you read, think about the following:

What has happened before this scene? What happens after this scene?

How does Shakespeare present Duncan in this extract?

How does Shakespeare present Macbeth in this extract?

Exam-style question

In this extract, Duncan is thanking Macbeth and Banquo for their part in the victory over the invading Norwegian army. The Thane of Cawdor has been hanged for treachery and Macbeth has been given his title, just as the witches predicted.

Extract A | Act 1 Scene 4 of Macbeth

MACBETH
The service and the loyalty I owe,
In doing it, pays itself. Your Highness' part
Is to receive our duties; and our duties
Are to your throne and state, children and servants,
5   Which do but what they should, by doing every thing
Safe toward your love and honour.
DUNCAN
          Welcome hither:
I have begun to plant thee, and will labour
To make thee full of growing. Noble Banquo,
10   That hast no less deserved, nor must be known
No less to have done so. Let me infold thee
And hold thee to my heart.
BANQUO
          There if I grow,
The harvest is your own.
DUNCAN
15   My plenteous joys,
Wanton in fulness, seek to hide themselves
In drops of sorrow. Sons, kinsmen, Thanes,
And you whose places are the nearest, know
We will establish our estate upon
20   Our eldest, Malcolm, whom we name hereafter
The Prince of Cumberland; which honour must
Not unaccompanied invest him only,
But signs of nobleness, like stars, shall shine
On all deservers. From hence to Inverness,
25   And bind us further to you.
MACBETH
The rest is labour, which is not used for you:
I'll be myself the harbinger and make joyful
The hearing of my wife with your approach;
So humbly take my leave.
DUNCAN
30   My worthy Cawdor!
MACBETH
[Aside] The Prince of Cumberland! That is a step
On which I must fall down, or else o'erleap,
For in my way it lies. Stars, hide your fires;
Let not light see my black and deep desires.
35   The eye wink at the hand; yet let that be,
Which the eye fears, when it is done, to see.
[Exit.]

1 How do I choose the points I need to make?

The first thing you need to do is to identify which parts of the extract you can explore further in your response to the question.

Look again at the **first part of** the exam-style question you are tackling.

Exam-style question

Explore how Shakespeare presents the character of Duncan as a leader in this extract.

(1) Now look through the extract, focusing on each speech in turn.

1. | Macbeth expresses his loyalty and duty to King Duncan [lines 1–6]

2. | Duncan welcomes and praises Macbeth and Banquo [lines 7–12]

3. | Banquo expresses his thanks and loyalty to Duncan [lines 13–14]

4. | Duncan reveals that his son, Malcolm, will be king after him [lines 15–25]

5. | Macbeth will tell his wife that Duncan will be staying at their castle [26–29]

6. | Macbeth thinks he will have to remove Malcolm if he wants to be king [lines 31–36]

a) Decide ✓ which **three** speeches reveal most about how Shakespeare presents the character of Duncan as a leader. Label 🖉 them **A**, **B** and **C**.

Think about:
• how Duncan uses his power and how he acts as king
• how the other characters in the extract respond to him.

b) Note 🖉 below what each of the speeches you have chosen reveals about how Shakespeare presents the character of Duncan as a leader.

A

B

C

2 How do I develop my analysis?

To develop your analysis, you need to think about what the characters say, why they say it, and what this reveals about the aspect of the play that you are exploring. Your ideas need to be supported by evidence from the extract.

Look again at the exam-style question you are exploring.

Exam-style question

Explore how Shakespeare presents the character of Duncan as a leader in this extract.

(1) Now look at one speech from the extract that reveals something about the character of Duncan as a leader:

DUNCAN
      Welcome hither:
I have begun to plant thee, and will labour
To make thee full of growing. Noble Banquo,
That hast no less deserved, nor must be known
No less to have done so. Let me infold thee
And hold thee to my heart.

Banquo and Macbeth have just won a great victory for Duncan and kept his kingdom safe from the invading Norwegian army.

(a) What does Duncan say in this speech? Sum it up ✎ in a **few** words.

....

(b) Why is Duncan saying this? Write ✎ **one** or **two** sentences explaining your ideas.

....

....

....

(c) Look again at your answers above. What does this speech suggest about Duncan as a leader? Note down ✎ some ideas.

....

....

....

(d) Which lines show this most clearly? Choose **two** short quotations and underline Ⓐ them.

(2) Now choose another speech from the extract that reveals something about the character of Duncan as a leader.

(a) Annotate ✎ the text on page 10, noting down:
- what the character says
- why they say it
- what it reveals about Duncan as a leader.

(b) Then underline Ⓐ **two** short quotations to support your ideas.

③ How do I structure a paragraph of analysis?

Each paragraph of your analysis should include:
- a key point focusing on the key words in the question
- evidence from the text to support your point
- comments on the evidence and its impact
- a response to the question.

> You can build your skill in analysing the extract in more depth and detail in Unit 3.

Look at the sentences from one paragraph of a student's response to this exam-style question.

Exam-style question

Explore how Shakespeare presents the character of Duncan as a leader in this extract.

① Tick ✓ the sentences you would include in a paragraph in response to the exam-style question.

		✓	✏
A	Shakespeare presents King Duncan as warm, generous and grateful for Macbeth and Banquo's victory over the Norwegian army.	☐	☐
B	Duncan uses his power in a positive way, rewarding his people for their help and support.	☐	☐
C	Duncan tells Macbeth that he will 'labour / To make thee full of growing', suggesting that Duncan will reward Macbeth with more honours and titles if he remains loyal and fights hard for Duncan.	☐	☐
D	Duncan calls Banquo 'Noble' and embraces him: 'Let me infold thee / And hold thee to my heart', suggesting he feels respect and affection for him.	☐	☐
E	The role of king is presented almost like the role of a father, caring for his family.	☐	☐
F	Shakespeare presents Duncan's leadership as positive and caring because he does not take his power, or the people he has power over, for granted.	☐	☐

② How would you sequence your chosen sentences in a paragraph? Number ✏ them.

③ Write ✏ a paragraph on paper using your chosen sentences and linking them with some or all of the following phrases or some of your own.

Similarly	This shows that	It suggests that	For example,	It could be argued that

④ Look at the sentences you have chosen and sequenced.

   a Which sentences make a key point? Label ✏ them '**Key point**'.

   b Which support a key point using evidence? Label ✏ them '**Evidence**'.

   c Which comment on the evidence and its impact? Label ✏ them '**Comment**'.

   d Which show the writer's response to the question? Label ✏ them '**Response**'.

Analysing the extract

To analyse the extract effectively, you need to:
- identify the parts of the extract that are relevant to the question
- explore what these parts suggest about the focus of the question
- structure your paragraphs of analysis to include a key point supported by evidence, a comment on its impact and a response to the question.

Look again at the **first part of** the exam-style question you saw at the start of the unit.

Exam-style question

Explore how Shakespeare presents the character of Duncan as a leader in this extract.

① Look at this paragraph, taken from a student's response to this question. It focuses on the extract on page 10, Extract A.

> In this extract, King Duncan appears to be a good leader, using his power to reward those who are loyal to him and fight for him. Macbeth has returned victorious from battle, and has been rewarded for his loyalty with the title of Thane of Cawdor. Duncan seems to promise that Macbeth will continue to be rewarded more if he continues to please Duncan: 'I have begun to plant thee, and will labour / To make thee full of growing.' While this seems to be a perfect picture of a loyal subject and a grateful king, it could be argued that Duncan is bribing Macbeth with the title of Thane of Cawdor to make sure he stays loyal. Furthermore, this extract comes just after Duncan has had the previous Thane of Cawdor executed for treachery. So this part of the play suggests that, in order to keep power, you must repay loyalty, but be cruel and ruthless when your power is challenged.

a Which of the following has this student achieved? Tick ✓ them.

A Identified a part of the extract that is relevant to the question.

B Explored what it suggests about the focus of the question.

C Made a key point.

D Supported it with evidence.

E Commented on its impact.

F Responded to the question.

b Highlight 🖉 and label 🖉 where in the paragraph this student has achieved C, D, E and F.

Your turn!

You are now going to **write one or two paragraphs** in response to the exam-style question below, focusing on **one or two of the speeches** in the extract on page 10.

MACBETH

The service and the loyalty I owe,
In doing it, pays itself. Your Highness' part
Is to receive our duties; and our duties
Are to your throne and state, children and servants,
Which do but what they should, by doing every thing
Safe toward your love and honour.

DUNCAN

My plenteous joys,
Wanton in fulness, seek to hide themselves
In drops of sorrow. Sons, kinsmen, thanes,
And you whose places are the nearest, know
We will establish our estate upon
Our eldest, Malcolm, whom we name hereafter
The Prince of Cumberland; which honour must
Not unaccompanied invest him only,
But signs of nobleness, like stars, shall shine
On all deservers.

Exam-style question

Explore how Shakespeare presents the character of Duncan as a leader in this extract.

Use the questions below to gather some ideas you could use in your response.

(1) Look at Macbeth's speech from the extract above. What does this suggest about Duncan as a leader? Make notes ✎

....

....

....

(2) Look at Duncan's speech from the extract above. What does this suggest about Duncan as a leader? Make notes ✎

....

....

....

(3) Now think about both speeches. Make notes ✎ on how is Shakespeare presenting the character of Duncan as a leader. You may want to use some of the ideas below, or use your own.

respected	affectionate	generous	fatherly	manipulative	wise

....

....

....

(4) Underline Ⓐ short, relevant quotations in the speeches above that you can use in your response.

(5) On paper, write ✎ **one** or **two** paragraphs in response to the exam-style question above.

Review your skills

Check up

Review your response to the exam-style question on page 15. Tick ✓ the column to show how well you think you have done each of the following.

	Not quite ✓	Nearly there ✓	Got it! ✓
made a relevant key point	☐	☐	☐
supported my key point with relevant evidence	☐	☐	☐
commented on the impact of my evidence	☐	☐	☐
responded to the question	☐	☐	☐

Look over all of your work in this unit. Note 🖉 down the **three** most important things to remember when planning your response.

1. ....

2. ....

3. ....

Need more practice?

Here is another exam-style question, this time relating to the extract from Act 1 Scene 2 on page 73 (Extract A).

Exam-style question

a Explore how Shakespeare presents the character of Macbeth in this extract.

Refer closely to the extract in your answer. (20 marks)

Write 🖉 **one** or **two** paragraphs in response to this question, focusing on the extract only.

You'll find some suggested ideas in the Answers section.

How confident do you feel about each of these **skills?** Colour 🖉 in the bars.

1 How do I choose the points I need to make?

2 How do I develop my analysis?

3 How do I structure a paragraph of analysis?

③ Commenting on the writer's choices in the extract

This unit will help you to comment on Shakespeare's choices in the extract from *Macbeth*. The skills you will build are to:

- identify relevant language choices to comment on
- identify relevant structural choices to comment on
- make effective comments on the writer's choices.

In the exam you will face questions like the one below. This is about the extract on the next page. At the end of the unit you will **write one or two paragraphs** in response to the **first part** of this question.

Exam-style question

a Explore how Shakespeare presents the character of Lady Macbeth as controlling and manipulative in this extract.

  Refer closely to the extract in your answer. **(20 marks)**

b This extract shows Lady Macbeth's ruthless ambitions for her husband.

  Explain the importance of ruthless ambition elsewhere in the play.

  In your answer you must consider:

  - how ruthless ambition is shown
  - the reasons that characters are ruthlessly ambitious.

  You should refer to the context of the play in your answer. **(20 marks)**

Before you tackle the question you will work through three key questions in the **skills boosts** to help you comment on the writer's choices in the extract.

① How do I identify significant language choices? ② How do I identify significant structural choices? ③ How do I comment on the writer's choices?

Read the extract on the next page from Act 1 Scene 5 of *Macbeth*.

As you read, think about the following: ✓

| What has happened before this scene? What happens after this scene? | How does Shakespeare present Lady Macbeth in this extract? | How does Shakespeare present Macbeth in this extract? |

In this extract, Macbeth returns home and tells his wife that the king, Duncan, will be staying with them that night. Lady Macbeth has learned of the witches' predictions: Macbeth will be king. She knows that her husband is ambitious and has resolved to persuade him to kill the king.

Extract A | Act 1 Scene 5 of *Macbeth*

Enter MACBETH

LADY MACBETH
        Great Glamis! worthy Cawdor!
Greater than both, by the all-hail hereafter!
Thy letters have transported me beyond
This ignorant present, and I feel now
5   The future in the instant.

MACBETH
        My dearest love,
Duncan comes here tonight.

LADY MACBETH
        And when goes hence?

MACBETH
Tomorrow, as he purposes.

LADY MACBETH
10   O, never
Shall sun that morrow see!
Your face, my Thane, is as a book where men
May read strange matters. To beguile the time,
Look like the time; bear welcome in your eye,
15   Your hand, your tongue: look like the innocent flower,
But be the serpent under't. He that's coming
Must be provided for: and you shall put
This night's great business into my dispatch;
Which shall to all our nights and days to come
20   Give solely sovereign sway and masterdom.

MACBETH
We will speak further.

LADY MACBETH
        Only look up clear;
To alter favour ever is to fear:
Leave all the rest to me.

Exeunt

1 How do I identify significant language choices?

The language that Shakespeare gives each character in a scene or extract can reveal a great deal about their thoughts, motivations and relationships.

1 Look at the lines that Shakespeare gives Lady Macbeth at the start of Extract A on page 18.

Lady Macbeth

> Great Glamis! worthy Cawdor!
> Greater than both, by the all-hail hereafter!

a In this speech, Lady Macbeth is both flattering Macbeth and reminding him that he could be king. Which words make this clearest? Circle Ⓐ **one** or **two** that are most significant.

b What does Shakespeare's choice of these words or phrases suggest about the character of Lady Macbeth and/or her relationship with Macbeth? Write ✏️ **one** or **two** sentences summing up your ideas.

....

....

....

2 Now look at two more sections of Lady Macbeth's speeches in the extract below.

a Annotate ✏️ each speech, noting your thoughts on these questions:

i What does Lady Macbeth say in this speech?

ii Why is Lady Macbeth saying this?

b Which **one** or **two** words or phrases in the speech highlight or emphasise what she is saying and the reason she is saying it most clearly? Circle Ⓐ them.

c What does each word or phrase you have circled suggest about the character of Lady Macbeth and/or her relationship with Macbeth? Annotate ✏️ the words and phrases you have circled.

A

> Your face, my Thane, is as a book where men
> May read strange matters. To beguile the time,
> Look like the time; bear welcome in your eye,
> Your hand, your tongue: look like the innocent flower,
> But be the serpent under't.

B

> Only look up clear;
> To alter favour ever is to fear:
> Leave all the rest to me.

Lady Macbeth

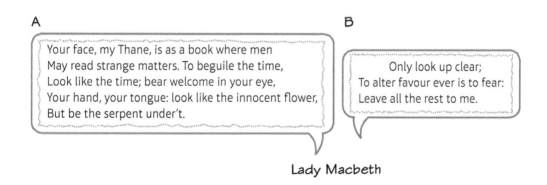

How do I identify significant structural choices?

When you think about Shakespeare's structural choices, think about how actors might perform the lines, and the impression this might create for the audience.

Look at these lines from the extract.

> **MACBETH**
>   My dearest love,
> Duncan comes here tonight.
> **LADY MACBETH**
>   And when goes hence?
> **MACBETH**
> Tomorrow, as he purposes.

1 **a** How would you describe the mood of this conversation? Circle Ⓐ **one** or **two** of the ideas below, or add ✐ your own.

tense	dramatic	excited	nervous	awkward	hurried

....

....

b How does the **length** of the lines, and the **pace** at which the actors might deliver them, contribute to this mood? Write ✐ **one** or **two** sentences explaining your ideas.

....

....

....

2 Now look at the whole extract.

a Which character has the most lines? Cross out ⊖ all or part of the sentences below to sum up your ideas.

  i   Lady Macbeth / Macbeth says much less than Lady Macbeth / Macbeth.

  ii Lady Macbeth / Macbeth does most of the talking.

  iii The two characters have a similar amount of lines.

b Look at your answer to question **2** **a** above. What does this suggest about:

- Macbeth's character, how he is feeling, and his relationship with his wife
- Lady Macbeth's character, how she is feeling, and her relationship with her husband?

Write ✐ **one** or **two** sentences, summing up your ideas.

....

....

....

How do I comment on the writer's choices?

An effective comment on the writer's choices highlights the **choice** the writer has made, and comments on its **effect**.

Look at some of the different kinds of comment on **language** and **structure** you could make on Lady Macbeth's final line from Extract A on page 18.

> Leave all the rest to me.   **Lady Macbeth**

Language

You can comment on...	choice	+	effect	
• the kind of language in the whole quotation	Simple, monosyllabic language		suggests her blunt, forceful tone.	☐
• a specific type of word	The imperative verb 'Leave'		shows her dominance over Macbeth.	☐
• the connotations or implications of a specific word or phrase.	The phrase 'the rest'		suggests she is taking control of almost all of the plan to kill Duncan.	☐

Structure

You can comment on...	choice	+	effect	
• the line's position in the scene	This is the final line of the scene		suggesting that Lady Macbeth gets the last word in this discussion.	☐
• the length of the line(s)	This short line		suggests an emphatic, unarguable tone.	☐
• the order of the words or ideas in the line(s).	The final word of this line, 'me',		suggests that Lady Macbeth is in control.	☐

(1) Which of these would you include in your comments? Tick ✓ them.

Now think about another part of Lady Macbeth's speech.

> look like the innocent flower,
> But be the serpent under't.

(2) Write ✐ **one** or **two** sentences commenting on Shakespeare's choices of language and structure in this section.

Think about: how Shakespeare uses **contrast** to structure these lines.

....

....

....

Commenting on the writer's choices in the extract

To comment effectively on Shakespeare's choices in the extract, you need to:

- identify relevant evidence from the extract to support your ideas
- select significant language and/or structural choices in the evidence you have identified
- highlight in your evidence the choices that Shakespeare has made and comment on their effect.

(For more help on structuring a paragraph of analysis, see Unit 2.)

Look again at this exam-style question you saw at the start of the unit.

Exam-style question

Explore how Shakespeare presents the character of Lady Macbeth as controlling and manipulative in this extract.

Can you identify all the different things the student has included in this paragraph? Link ✐ the annotations to the paragraph to show where the student has included them.

Key features of an effective paragraph of analysis:

| key point focusing on the key words in the question |

| evidence from the text to support your point |

| comments on the evidence and its impact |

| a response to the question |

As soon as Macbeth appears at the start of the extract, Lady Macbeth ruthlessly dominates the scene and tries to influence him. She welcomes him home, calling him 'Great Glamis! worthy Cawdor!' These short, emphatic exclamations suggest her excitement and are meant to flatter Macbeth. She uses the positive adjectives 'great' and 'worthy' to boost his confidence and make him feel important. She also uses his new title of 'Cawdor' to remind him of the witches' prediction that has already come true, and the rest of the prediction which she wants him to make come true. Lady Macbeth doubts her husband will be ruthless enough to do this, and so feels she must flatter and manipulate him to be as ruthless and ambitious as she is.

Key features of an effective comment on the writer's choices:

| a comment on language choice(s) |

| a comment on structural choice(s) |

Your turn!

You are now going to **write one or two paragraphs** in response to the **first part** of the exam-style question.

> **Exam-style question**
>
> **a** Explore how Shakespeare presents the character of Lady Macbeth as controlling and manipulative in this extract.
>
> Refer closely to the extract in your answer. **(20 marks)**

① Write 🖉 a sentence summing up **one** way in which Lady Macbeth is presented as controlling and manipulative in the extract.

....

....

② Focus on **one** speech in the extract on page 18 that supports your answer to question ① above and circle Ⓐ it.

③ Now look closely at the speech you have chosen. Select a short quotation that clearly supports your answer to question ① above. Underline Ⓐ it on page 18.

④ Think about words or phrases in your chosen quotation that make a significant contribution to your answer to question ① above.

   a Which words or phrases reveal something significant about Lady Macbeth, her thoughts, attitudes or relationship with Macbeth? Circle Ⓐ them on page 18.

   b What do those words and phrases suggest about Lady Macbeth? Annotate 🖉 them.

⑤ Now think about Shakespeare's structural choices in your chosen quotation. Think about:

   • the line's position in the scene
   • the length of the line(s)
   • the order of the words or ideas in the line(s).

   Do Shakespeare's structural choices in your chosen quotation make a significant contribution to your answer to question ① above? How? Annotate 🖉 your chosen quotation with your ideas.

⑥ Using all the ideas you have noted, write 🖉 **one** paragraph on paper in response to the exam-style question above.

⑦ Write 🖉 a sentence summing up **another** way in which Lady Macbeth is presented as controlling and manipulative in the extract.

....

....

⑧ Focus on one speech in the extract that supports your answer to question ⑦ above. Circle Ⓐ it on page 18, then repeat questions ③–⑥.

Review your skills

Check up

Review your response to the exam-style question on page 23. Tick ✓ the column to show how well you think you have done each of the following.

	Not quite ✓	Nearly there ✓	Got it! ✓
structured an effective paragraph of analysis in response to the question	☐	☐	☐
commented on Shakespeare's language choices	☐	☐	☐
commented on Shakespeare's structural choices	☐	☐	☐

Look over all of your work in this unit. Note ✏ down the **three** most important things to remember when planning your response.

1. ....

2. ....

3. ....

Need more practice?

Here is another exam-style question, this time relating to the extract from Act 3 Scene 1 on page 74 (Extract B).

Exam-style question

a Explore how Shakespeare presents the character of Banquo in this extract.

Refer closely to the extract in your answer. **(20 marks)**

Write ✏ **one** or **two** paragraphs in response to this question. You'll find some suggested ideas in the Answers section.

How confident do you feel about each of these skills? Colour ✏ in the bars.

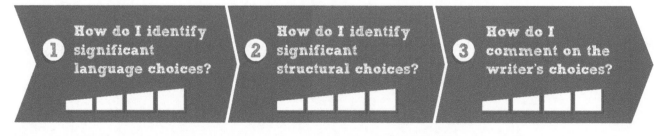

4 Exploring characters

This unit will help you to explore how the characters are presented in the play, and help you to develop your response to them. The skills you will build are to:

- explore the presentation of character in the extract
- explore the presentation of character in the context of the whole play
- explore different responses to characters.

In the exam you will face questions like the one below. This is about the extract on the next page. At the end of the unit you will **plan and write one or two paragraphs** in response to the **first part** of this question.

Exam-style question

a Explore how Shakespeare presents the character of Macbeth as a good man in this extract.
   Refer closely to the extract in your answer.   (20 marks)

b This extract shows Macbeth's fear.
   Explain the importance of fear elsewhere in the play.
   In your answer you must consider:
   - how fear is shown
   - the reasons that characters show fear.
   You should refer to the context of the play in your answer.   (20 marks)

Before you tackle the question you will work through three key questions in the **skills boosts** to help you explore the play's themes and characters.

 How do I track the main characters in the play?   **How do I comment on character at key points of the play?**   **How can I explore the presentation of a character in the extract?**

Read the extract on the next page from Act 1 Scene 7 of Macbeth.

As you read, think about the following: ⊘

↙   ↓   ↘

What has happened before this scene? What happens after this scene?	How does Shakespeare present Lady Macbeth in this extract?	How does Shakespeare present Macbeth in this extract?

Exam-style question

In this extract, Macbeth and Lady Macbeth discuss their plan to murder King Duncan, who is staying in Macbeth's castle. Macbeth has realised how wrong and how risky it would be to murder Duncan and has decided that he cannot do it.

Extract A | Act 1 Scene 7 of Macbeth

MACBETH
We will proceed no further in this business:
He hath honour'd me of late; and I have bought
Golden opinions from all sorts of people,
Which would be worn now in their newest gloss,
5   Not cast aside so soon.
LADY MACBETH
Was the hope drunk
Wherein you dress'd yourself? Hath it slept since?
And wakes it now, to look so green and pale
At what it did so freely? From this time
10   Such I account thy love. Art thou afeard
To be the same in thine own act and valour
As thou art in desire? Wouldst thou have that
Which thou esteem'st the ornament of life,
And live a coward in thine own esteem,
15   Letting 'I dare not' wait upon 'I would,'
Like the poor cat i' the adage?
MACBETH
Prithee, peace:
I dare do all that may become a man;
Who dares do more is none.
LADY MACBETH
20   What beast was't, then,
That made you break this enterprise to me?
When you durst do it, then you were a man;
And, to be more than what you were, you would
Be so much more the man. Nor time nor place
25   Did then adhere, and yet you would make both:
They have made themselves, and that their fitness now
Does unmake you. I have given suck, and know
How tender 'tis to love the babe that milks me:
I would, while it was smiling in my face,
30   Have pluck'd my nipple from his boneless gums,
And dash'd the brains out, had I so sworn as you
Have done to this.
MACBETH
If we should fail?
LADY MACBETH
We fail!
35   But screw your courage to the sticking-place,
And we'll not fail.

How do I track the main characters in the play?

To write effectively about how Shakespeare presents a character in the extract, it is helpful to think about how Shakespeare presents their character in the whole play, and how their character changes and develops.

(1) Think about how Macbeth is presented at the **start** of the play.
In **Act 1**:

- we hear about 'brave Macbeth' in battle in Act 1 Scene 2

- he hears the witches' predictions in Act 1 Scene 3

- in Act 1 Scene 4, he swears loyalty to Duncan while hiding his 'deep and dark desires'

- he fears his ambition and is reluctant to kill Duncan in Act 1 Scenes 5 and 7

How would you sum up the character of Macbeth at the start of the play? Tick ✓ any of the words below and/or add ✐ your own idea.

brave	loyal	dishonest	ruthless	ambitious	superstitious	manipulative	frightened	
☐	☐	☐	☐	☐	☐	☐	☐	

(2) Now think about Macbeth at the **end** of the play. In **Act 5**:

- after meeting the witches in Act 4, he believes he is invincible

- in Act 5 Scene 3, he does not seem surprised or upset at Lady Macbeth's death and has 'almost forgot the taste of fears'

- he is killed by Macduff in Act 5 scene 8

How would you sum up the character of Macbeth at the end of the play? Note ✐ up to **five** words.

Look at the words you chose to describe him in question (1). What has changed?

....

(3) Now look at some of the key scenes showing the development of the character of Macbeth.

| 2.2 | Macbeth murders King Duncan. He fears he shall 'sleep no more'. | /10 |

| 3.4 | Macbeth sees Banquo's ghost. Macbeth says he is 'in blood / Stepped in so far that, should I wade no more, / Returning were as tedious as go o'er.' | /10 |

| 3.2 | Macbeth tells his wife that his mind is 'full of scorpions' but not that he has arranged Banquo's murder. | /10 |

| 4.2 | Macbeth has Macduff's wife and children murdered. | /10 |

| 3.3 | Macbeth has Banquo murdered. | /10 |

(a) How significant is each of these scenes in showing the change in Macbeth's character from the start to the end of the play? Give ✐ each one a mark out of ten: 1/10 = not at all significant; 10/10 = highly significant.

(b) Write ✐ **one** or **two** sentences summing up how the character of Macbeth develops and changes during the course of the play.

....

....

2 How do I comment on character at key points of the play?

When you think about how a character is presented in the extract, you also need to think about the extract in the context of the whole play: what impressions of this character does the audience have at this point in the play? How might these impressions be changed by their presentation in the extract? How will these impressions be affected later in the play?

① Look at these key moments in the development of the character of Lady Macbeth.

> • When she first appears in the play, in Act 1 Scene 5, ...
>
> ....
>
> • In Act 1 Scene 7, she persuades her husband to overcome his fears and kill King Duncan.
>
> • In Act 2 Scene 2, she assures Macbeth that 'a little water clears us of this deed'.
>
> • In Act 3 Scene 2, she admits to herself that she is anxious about the murder of Duncan.
>
> • In her final appearance in the play, in Act 5 Scene 1, ...
>
> ....
>
> • Near the end of the play, we are told that ....
>
> ....

a Complete ✐ the notes above, summing up how Lady Macbeth is presented at the **start** and **end** of the play.

b How does Lady Macbeth's character develop during the course of the play? Write ✐ **two** or **three** sentences summing up your ideas.

....

....

....

② Look again at the extract on page 26.

a Now look at the list of Lady Macbeth's key moments above. Where does the extract on page 26 come in this list? Mark ✐ that point in the list with an asterisk *.

b What impression might the audience have of Lady Macbeth at this point in the play? Write ✐ **one** or **two** sentences explaining your ideas.

....

....

c Which key moments in the development of Lady Macbeth's character above help to **confirm** this impression? Tick ✓ them.

d Which key moments in the development of Lady Macbeth's character above help to **change** this impression? Cross ✗ them.

e What might this suggest about the character of Lady Macbeth in this extract? On paper write ✐ **one** or **two** sentences explaining your ideas.

3 How can I explore the presentation of a character in the extract?

One way in which you can effectively explore the presentation of character is to consider different possible responses and interpretations.

① Look at some of these quotations from the extract on page 26. For each quotation, note down two possible interpretations. The first two have been completed to help you.

A
> **MACBETH**
> We will proceed no further in this business:
> He hath honour'd me of late; and I have bought
> Golden opinions from all sorts of people

Why is Macbeth reluctant to kill Duncan?

Is it because it would be the wrong thing to do? Or because he is a proud, vain man, happy with people's 'golden opinions' of him?

Why is Lady Macbeth trying to manipulate her husband in this way?

Is it because she is so supportive of him and his ambitions? Or because she is desperate to achieve her own ambitions?

> **LADY MACBETH**
> From this time
> Such I account thy love.
B

C
> **MACBETH**
> Prithee, peace:
> I dare do all that may become a man;
> Who dares do more is none.

Macbeth will only do those things that 'become a man', that are fitting and proper for a man to do. Does he really think this?

He could be saying it because ....

Or ....

Would Lady Macbeth really do this? Why is she saying it?

Is it because ....

....

Or because ....

....

> **LADY MACBETH**
> I have given suck, and know
> How tender 'tis to love the babe that milks me:
> I would, while it was smiling in my face,
> Have pluck'd my nipple from his boneless gums,
> And dash'd the brains out, had I so sworn as you
> Have done to this.
D

E
> **MACBETH**
> If we should fail?

What is Macbeth worried about? Are these the worries of a good man?

He could be saying it because ....

Or ....

② Write **one** or **two** sentences about each character, summing up and explaining your ideas.

....
....
....
....

Exploring characters

To explore effectively how a character is presented in an extract from *Macbeth*, you need to:

- consider how the character is presented in the whole play
- think about the extract in the context of the whole play: how might the audience's response to the character be changed by their presentation in the extract?
- consider different ways in which an audience might respond to the character.

Look again at this exam-style question you saw at the start of the unit.

Exam-style question

Explore how Shakespeare presents the character of Macbeth as a good man in this extract.

Look at these two paragraphs, written by a student in response to the exam-style question above.

> In some ways, Macbeth is presented as a good man at this point in the play. Although he is ambitious to be king, he is reluctant to murder Duncan in order to achieve that ambition. He firmly tells his wife that 'We will proceed no further in this business', the phrase 'we will' suggesting that he is trying to be dominant and reject his wife's demands. However, the reasons he gives suggest that perhaps he is not as good as he appears. He tells his wife that he has been 'honour'd' by Duncan and has 'bought / Golden opinions from all sorts of people'. The word 'golden' suggests how high these opinions are, and how much he values them, which suggests that he is more worried about his reputation as a good man than actually acting like one.
>
> The presentation of Lady Macbeth in this extract also makes Macbeth appear a better man than he really is. She is shown to be controlling, manipulative and ruthless, telling her husband that she will 'account his love' according to whether he will kill Duncan. Her call for 'direst cruelty' and Duncan's 'golden opinions' of Macbeth, both of which have been clearly shown earlier in the play, could create the impression that Macbeth is a good man who is being manipulated by his evil wife.

(1) Identify the sentences in these paragraphs where this student has commented on **the presentation of Macbeth in the extract**. Underline (A) and label (✐) them **'extract'**.

(2) Identify the sentences in these paragraphs where this student has commented on how **other parts of the play might affect the audience's response to Macbeth** in this part of the play. Underline (A) and label (✐) them **'other parts'**.

(3) Identify the sentences in these paragraphs where this student has considered **different ways in which an audience might respond** to Macbeth at this point in the play. Underline (A) and label (✐) them **'different responses'**.

Your turn!

You are now going to write **two** paragraphs in response to the **first part** of the exam-style question.

Exam-style question

> **a** Explore how Shakespeare presents the character of Macbeth as a good man in this extract. Refer closely to the extract in your answer. **(20 marks)**

1 Think about how Macbeth is presented in the extract on page 26. How good a man does he appear to be? Mark  the scale below with an asterisk * to show where you would position the character of Macbeth at this point in the play.

```
  0    1    2    3    4    5    6    7    8    9    10
 Evil                                            Good
```

2 Note down **at least three** quotations from the extract that support your response to the presentation of Macbeth in the extract.

....

....

....

....

....

3 Look at the quotations you have selected. Annotate them, highlighting any language or structural choices that you could comment on in your response.

4 Which other parts of the play that come **before** this extract might **affect** your response to the character of Macbeth? Note them down.

....

....

....

5 Which other parts of the play that come **after** this extract might **confirm** your view of Macbeth in the extract? Note them down.

....

....

....

6 Look carefully over your notes above, then write **two** paragraphs in response to the exam-style question on paper.

Review your skills

Check up

Review your response to the exam-style question on page 31. Tick ✓ the column to show how well you think you have done each of the following.

	Not quite ✓	Nearly there ✓	Got it! ✓
selected and commented on relevant evidence from the extract	☐	☐	☐
considered the impact of other parts of the play on my response to the character of Macbeth in the extract	☐	☐	☐
considered different possible responses to the character of Macbeth in the extract	☐	☐	☐

Look over all of your work in this unit. Note ✐ down the **three** most important things to remember when exploring the presentation of a character in an extract.

1. ....

2. ....

3. ....

Need more practice?

Here is another exam-style question, this time relating to the extract from Act 3 Scene 2 on page 75.

Exam-style question

a Explore how Shakespeare presents Macbeth's and Lady Macbeth's feelings in this extract.
   Refer closely to the extract in your answer.   **(20 marks)**

Write ✐ **two** paragraphs in response to this question.

Aim to:

• select and comment on relevant evidence from the extract
• consider the impact of other parts of the play on your response to Macbeth and Lady Macbeth in the extract
• consider different possible responses to Macbeth and Lady Macbeth in the extract.

You'll find some suggested ideas in the Answers section.

How confident do you feel about each of these **skills**? Colour ✐ in the bars.

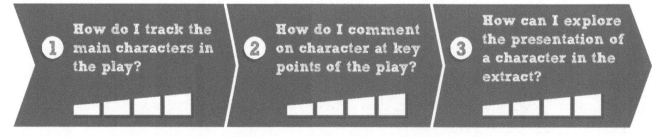

1 How do I track the main characters in the play?

2 How do I comment on character at key points of the play?

3 How can I explore the presentation of a character in the extract?

⑤ Exploring themes

This unit will help you to explore how the themes of *Macbeth* are presented in the play, and help you to develop your response to them. The skills you will build are to:

- track how themes are presented in the play
- comment on the presentation of themes at a key point in the play
- explore the themes of the play.

In the exam you will face questions like the one below. This is about the extract on the next page. At the end of the unit you will **plan and write a response** to the **second part** of this question.

Exam-style question

a Explore how Shakespeare presents Macbeth's relationship with Lady Macbeth in this extract.
Refer closely to the extract in your answer.   **(20 marks)**

b In this extract we see the effect of guilt on Macbeth.
Explain the importance of guilt elsewhere in the play.
In your answer you must consider:
- how guilt is shown
- how guilt affects characters in the play.
You should refer to the context of the play in your answer.   **(20 marks)**

Before you tackle the question you will work through three key questions in the **skills boosts** to help you explore the play's themes.

1 How do I track the themes of the play?   **2** How do I comment on a theme at key points of the play?   **3** How do I explore the themes of the play?

Read the extract on the next page from Act 2 Scene 2 of *Macbeth*.

As you read, think about the following: ⊘

What has happened before this scene? What happens after this scene?

How does Shakespeare present Macbeth's attitude to the murder of Duncan in this extract?

How does Shakespeare present Lady Macbeth's attitude to the murder of Duncan in this extract?

Exam-style question

In this extract, Macbeth tells Lady Macbeth that he heard the voices of Duncan's sons as he returned from murdering him. He still has Duncan's blood on his hands.

Extract A | Act 2 Scene 2 of Macbeth

> **MACBETH**
> This is a sorry sight.
> *Looking on his hands*
> **LADY MACBETH**
> A foolish thought, to say a sorry sight.
> **MACBETH**
> There's one did laugh in's sleep, and one cried 'Murder!'
> That they did wake each other: I stood and heard them:
> 5   But they did say their prayers, and address'd them
> Again to sleep.
> **LADY MACBETH**
> There are two lodged together.
> **MACBETH**
> One cried 'God bless us!' and 'Amen' the other;
> As they had seen me with these hangman's hands.
> 10   Listening their fear, I could not say 'Amen,'
> When they did say 'God bless us!'
> **LADY MACBETH**
> Consider it not so deeply.
> **MACBETH**
> But wherefore could not I pronounce 'Amen'?
> I had most need of blessing, and 'Amen'
> 15   Stuck in my throat.
> **LADY MACBETH**
> These deeds must not be thought
> After these ways; so, it will make us mad.
> **MACBETH**
> Methought I heard a voice cry 'Sleep no more!
> Macbeth does murder sleep', the innocent sleep,
> 20   Sleep that knits up the ravell'd sleeve of care,
> The death of each day's life, sore labour's bath,
> Balm of hurt minds, great nature's second course,
> Chief nourisher in life's feast,--
> **LADY MACBETH**
> What do you mean?
> **MACBETH**
> 25   Still it cried 'Sleep no more!' to all the house:
> 'Glamis hath murder'd sleep, and therefore Cawdor
> Shall sleep no more; Macbeth shall sleep no more.'

How do I track the themes of the play?

To explore the way in which Shakespeare develops a theme of the play, you need to identify key scenes in which that theme is featured.

1. Look at some of the **key themes** in *Macbeth* below. Complete 🖉 these notes by identifying a **key plot** event in which each theme is relevant.

power	
ambition	
good and evil	*Lady Macbeth calls upon the forces of evil to 'fill' her with 'direst cruelty'.*
violence	
the supernatural	
guilt	*Macbeth is filled with guilt after killing King Duncan.*
loyalty	

2. Some key scenes in the play feature two or more of the play's key themes. Look at Extract A from Act 2 Scene 2 on page 34.

   a. Tick ✓ any of the play's themes below that are relevant in this scene.

   b. Annotate 🖉 each theme that you have ticked, explaining why it is relevant.

   power ☐   good and evil ☐   guilt ☐   loyalty ☐

   ambition ☐   violence ☐   the supernatural ☐

Each of these key scenes from *Macbeth* explores the theme of guilt.

2.1 Macbeth prepares to murder Duncan and sees 'a dagger of the mind'. ☐

3.2 Lady Macbeth admits to herself that she is anxious about the murder of Duncan. Macbeth tells her that his mind is 'full of scorpions'. ☐

3.4 Macbeth sees Banquo's ghost. ☐

5.1 Lady Macbeth sleepwalks: 'will these hands ne'er be clean?' ☐

5.5 Lady Macbeth is dead. It is later suggested that she died by 'self and violent hands'. ☐

3. Which scenes would you focus on in your response to part **b** of the exam-style question on page 33? Tick ✓ **three**, annotating 🖉 each one to explain your choice.

2 How do I comment on a theme at key points of the play?

To investigate the way in which Shakespeare develops a theme of the play, you need to explore how it is presented in each key scene that you focus on.

1 Look at four key moments in the play at which the theme of **violence** is shown.

What does each key moment suggest about Shakespeare's presentation of violence? Draw lines linking each key moment to **one or more** of the statements below.

A In Act 1 Scene 2, we hear about Macbeth's victory in battle, when he 'unseam'd' Macdonwald and 'fix'd his head upon our battlements'.	**a** Violence is always wrong.
B In Act 2 Scene 2, Macbeth murders King Duncan.	**b** Violence always leads to more violence.
C In Act 4 Scene 2, Macbeth has Macduff's wife and children 'savagely slaughtered'.	**c** Violence is sometimes necessary and acceptable.
D At the end of the play, Macbeth is killed. His severed head is carried on stage.	**d** Violence always has negative consequences.

Now think about how the theme of **guilt** is shown in Extract A from Act 2 Scene 2 on page 34.

Remember: You cannot use the extract in your response to the second part of the exam question.

2 Look at two quotations from the extract.

Lady Macbeth

> These deeds must not be thought
> After these ways; so, it will make us mad.

Macbeth

> Still it cried 'Sleep no more!' to all the house:
> 'Glamis hath murder'd sleep, and therefore Cawdor
> Shall sleep no more; Macbeth shall sleep no more.'

....

....

....

....

....

a How do Macbeth and Lady Macbeth react to the murder of King Duncan? Note your ideas below each quotation. Think about:

- how each character expresses (or does not express) any feelings of guilt
- the impact that guilt can have.

b How does Shakespeare present the theme of guilt in this extract? Use your notes above to write one or two sentences explaining your ideas.

....

....

....

3 How do I explore the themes of the play?

One way in which you can explore how themes develop in *Macbeth* is to **compare** how they are presented in different key scenes in the play.

A **key theme** is an idea that Shakespeare explores in different ways at different points in the play. Look at some of the key scenes in which Shakespeare explores the theme of **power**.

> Duncan rewards his loyal Thanes while Macbeth plots to kill him and take his power.

> When Macbeth acts on the witches' predictions, Shakespeare shows their power over him.

> In persuading Macbeth to kill Duncan, Lady Macbeth shows her power over him.

> Macbeth murders Duncan in order to gain power.

> Macbeth has those who threaten his power murdered: Banquo and Macduff's family.

(1) How does Shakespeare present power in the play? Circle (A) any of the ideas below.

positive		neutral		negative	
exciting	rewarding	necessary	a great responsibility	corrupting	dangerous

(2) Now think about how Shakespeare presents the theme of **the supernatural** in the play.

  a Note down ✎ **three** significant points in the play where the supernatural is shown.

A .... B .... C ....

....

....

....

....

  b Now add ✎ to your notes above, describing how Shakespeare presents the supernatural in each of the significant scenes you have identified.

  c Review your notes, then write ✎ **one** or **two** sentences summing up your ideas about how Shakespeare presents the supernatural in *Macbeth*.

Think about:
- why these supernatural figures appear in the play
- the impact of the supernatural on the other characters
- the impact of the supernatural on the audience.

....

....

....

....

Exploring themes

To explore the themes in *Macbeth* effectively, you need to:

- identify significant key events in the play in which each theme is shown
- explore how the theme is shown in each of those key events
- compare how the theme is presented in those key events.

Look again at the exam-style question you saw at the start of the unit.

> **Exam-style question**
>
> In this extract we see the effect of guilt on Macbeth.
>
> Explain the importance of guilt elsewhere in the play.
>
> In your answer you must consider:
>
> - how guilt is shown
> - how guilt affects characters in the play.
>
> You should refer to the context of the play in your answer.　　　　　　　(20 marks)

Now look at these two paragraphs, written by a student in response to the exam-style question above.

> One way in which guilt is important in the play is in the character of Macbeth. In the first half of the play he shows guilt at the murders of Duncan and Banquo. Because he uses murderers to kill Banquo, Shakespeare suggests that Macbeth is trying to avoid the guilt he felt at the murder of Duncan. However, Shakespeare develops Macbeth's guilt, showing it in the form of Banquo's ghost. This suggests that Macbeth is literally being haunted by his feelings of guilt and is terrified of them. It is this guilt that helps the audience to have some sympathy for Macbeth as it shows that he is not completely inhuman and evil.
>
> However, in the second half of the play, Macbeth shows little guilt or remorse. He has Macduff's wife and children killed but, after he has ordered it to be done, does not mention it again. It seems that Macbeth is 'in blood stepped in so far' and so worried and obsessed with his life and his power falling apart, that he has lost his own feelings of guilt, suggesting that by the end of the play Shakespeare wants the audience to see him as either mad or evil.

1 Circle Ⓐ and label ✎ **all** the key scenes or events in the play that the student has referred to.

2 Underline Ⓐ and label ✎ where in these paragraphs the student **comments on** how Shakespeare presents guilt in these key scenes or events.

3 Underline Ⓐ and label ✎ where in these paragraphs the student **compares** key scenes or events in which guilt is presented to develop her ideas.

Your turn!

You are now going to **write your response** to the **second part** of the exam-style question.

Exam-style question

b In this extract we see the effect of guilt on Macbeth.

Explain the importance of guilt elsewhere in the play.

In your answer you must consider:

- how guilt is shown
- how guilt affects characters in the play.

You should refer to the context of the play in your answer. **(20 marks)**

1 Which key scenes or events in the play could you focus on in your response? Note 🖉 **four** below. Think about these questions.

? Which characters in the play show guilt? Which key scenes or events show this most clearly?

? Do these characters' feelings of guilt change in the play? Are there other key scenes or events in the play which show them in a different light?

1

2

3

4

2 Look carefully at each of the key scenes or events you have chosen. How is guilt presented in each one? Add 🖉 to your notes.

3 Now compare the presentation of guilt in the different key scenes or events you have chosen. What does your comparison suggest about the way in which guilt is presented in the play? Add 🖉 to your notes.

4 Write 🖉 your paragraphs in response to the exam-style question above on paper.

Review your skills

Check up

Review your response to the exam-style question on page 39. Tick ✓ the column to show how well you think you have done each of the following.

	Not quite ✓	Nearly there ✓	Got it! ✓
identified significant scenes or events in the play showing the theme of guilt	☐	☐	☐
commented on how guilt is presented in each significant scene or event	☐	☐	☐
developed my ideas by comparing how guilt is presented in key scenes or events	☐	☐	☐

Look over all of your work in this unit. Note ✏ down the **three** most important things to remember when writing about themes.

1. ....

2. ....

3. ....

Need more practice?

Here is another exam-style question, this time relating to the extract from Act 3 Scene 2 on page 75 (Extract C).

Exam-style question

a Explore how Shakespeare presents Macbeth's and Lady Macbeth's feelings in this extract.
Refer closely to the extract in your answer. **(20 marks)**

b This extract shows Lady Macbeth telling Macbeth to hide his true feelings and give the false appearance of being happy.
Explain the importance of false appearances elsewhere in the play.
In your answer you must consider:
• how false appearances are shown
• how false appearances affect those involved.
You should refer to the context of the play in your answer. **(20 marks)**

Write ✏ your response to the **second part** of this question. You'll find some suggested ideas in the Answers section.

How confident do you feel about each of these **skills**? Colour ✏ in the bars.

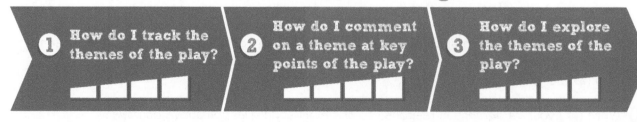

1 How do I track the themes of the play?

2 How do I comment on a theme at key points of the play?

3 How do I explore the themes of the play?

⑥ Planning to write about the whole play

This unit will help you to plan your response to the second part of the exam question. The skills you will build are to:

- develop a critical judgement in response to the focus of the question
- support your judgement with relevant points
- sequence your points to build a successful argument in support of your judgement.

In the exam you will face questions like the one below. This is about the extract on the next page. At the end of the unit you will **write your own response** to the **second part** of this question.

Exam-style question

a Explore how Shakespeare presents Lady Macbeth's relationships with Macbeth, and with Ross, Lennox and the other Lords in this extract.

Refer closely to the extract in your answer.   (20 marks)

b In this extract Macbeth has lost control of himself and the situation.

Explain the importance of power and control elsewhere in the play.

In your answer you must consider:

- how power is shown
- how power affects characters in the play.

You should refer to the context of the play in your answer.   (20 marks)

Before you tackle the question you will work through three key questions in the **skills boosts** to help you plan your response.

| ① How do I make a critical judgement? | ② How do I gather relevant points? | ③ How do I sequence my points? |

Read the extract on the next page from Act 3 Scene 4 of *Macbeth*.

As you read, think about the following: ✓

What has happened before this scene? What happens after this scene?

How does Shakespeare present Macbeth's thoughts and feelings in this extract?

How does Shakespeare present Lady Macbeth's thoughts and feelings in this extract?

In this extract, Macbeth and Lady Macbeth are holding a banquet to celebrate Macbeth becoming the King of Scotland. The ghost of Banquo has appeared and is sitting in Macbeth's place.

Extract A | Act 3 Scene 4 of *Macbeth*

ROSS
Please't your Highness
To grace us with your royal company.
MACBETH
The table's full.
LENNOX
Here is a place reserved, sir.
MACBETH
5   Where?
LENNOX
Here, my good lord. What is't that moves your Highness?
MACBETH
Which of you have done this?
LORDS
What, my good lord?
MACBETH
Thou canst not say I did it: never shake
10   Thy gory locks at me.
ROSS
Gentlemen, rise: his Highness is not well.
LADY MACBETH
Sit, worthy friends: my lord is often thus,
And hath been from his youth. Pray you, keep seat;
The fit is momentary; upon a thought
15   He will again be well. If much you note him,
You shall offend him and extend his passion:
Feed, and regard him not—Are you a man?
MACBETH
Ay, and a bold one, that dare look on that
Which might appal the devil.
LADY MACBETH
20   O proper stuff!
This is the very painting of your fear.
This is the air-drawn dagger which, you said,
Led you to Duncan. O, these flaws and starts,
Impostors to true fear, would well become
25   A woman's story at a winter's fire,
Authorised by her grandam. Shame itself!
Why do you make such faces? When all's done,
You look but on a stool.

How do I make a critical judgement?

Before you plan your written response, you need to make a **critical judgement** on the topic in the question. This means weighing up the key evidence in the play and coming to a conclusion: a sentence or two that sums up your ideas.

(1) One way to begin developing your critical judgement is to focus on the extract you are given in the first part of the question. Look at two quotations from the extract opposite.

Macbeth

> Thou canst not say I did it: never shake
> Thy gory locks at me.

Lady Macbeth

> Sit, worthy friends: my lord is often thus,
> And hath been from his youth. Pray you, keep seat;

....

....

....

....

a Who is in control in this scene? Note 🖉 your ideas below each quotation.

b Write 🖉 **one** or **two** sentences summing up your **critical judgement** on how the theme of power and control is presented in the extract.

....

....

....

(2) Now you need to develop your critical judgement by thinking about the theme of power and control **elsewhere in the play**. Look at these other scenes in which control is shown, or lost.

1.3, 4.1 The witches influence Macbeth with their predictions.	**1.5, 1.7** Lady Macbeth persuades her husband to kill Duncan.	
2.2 Macbeth panics after the murder of Duncan. His wife assures him that 'a little water clears us of this deed'.	**3.2** Macbeth plans to kill Banquo but does not reveal this to his wife.	
4.2 Macbeth has Macduff's family killed.	**5.8** Macbeth believes himself invincible but is killed.	

a Which of these scenes could be used as evidence to **support** or **develop** the critical judgement you made in question (1) **b** ? Tick ✓ them.

b Which of these scenes **contradict** the critical judgement you made? Cross ✗ them.

c Is your critical judgement on how the theme of power and control is presented in the extract relevant to the rest of the play? Or do you need to rethink it now that you have considered some of the other scenes in which power and control are relevant? Either tick ✓ your answer to question (1) **b**, or rewrite 🖉 it on a separate sheet of paper.

2 How do I gather relevant points?

You need to gather a range of points to support and develop the critical judgement you make in response to the second part of the exam question.

1. Think about how **power and control** are presented in the whole play.

   a. Look at the critical judgements about the presentation of power and control in *Macbeth* below. For each one, circle (A) a number to show whether you agree or disagree.

	Disagree	Unsure	Agree
A The desire for power leads to self-destruction.	1	2	3
B Ambitious people are very easily influenced and controlled.	1	2	3
C The more power and control human beings have, the more they want.	1	2	3
D The desire for power blinds characters' judgement and leads to ill-considered choices and the loss of self-control.	1	2	3
E The audience are encouraged to respect those who have gained power legitimately.	1	2	3

   b. Now look at some of the key scenes from the play below. Select key scenes that support each of the judgements you agreed with, labelling (✐) them **A, B, C**, etc, to show which judgement they support.

   | 1.3, 4.1 | The witches influence Macbeth with their predictions. | ☐ | 1.4 | Duncan rewards Macbeth with the title of Thane of Cawdor. Macbeth secretly plots to become king. | ☐ |

   | 1.5, 1.7 | Lady Macbeth persuades her husband to kill Duncan. | ☐ | 2.2 | Macbeth panics after the murder of Duncan. His wife assures him that 'a little water clears us of this deed'. | ☐ |

   | 3.2 | Macbeth plans to kill Banquo but does not reveal this to his wife. | ☐ | 4.2 | Macbeth has Macduff's family killed. | ☐ |

   | 5.1 | Lady Macbeth sleepwalks: 'will these hands ne'er be clean?' | ☐ | 5.8 | Macbeth believes himself invincible but is killed. | ☐ |

2. Review all of your answers on this page. Use them to note down (✐) **three** key points you might make in your response to the exam-style question. For each key point, note (✐) the key scenes from the play that you could refer to as evidence to support your point.

	Key point	Evidence
1		
2		
3		

3 How do I sequence my points?

You need to sequence your key points to build a logical argument that supports your critical judgement.

Look at this exam-style question, and one student's critical judgement in response to it.

Exam-style question

Explain the importance of power and control elsewhere in the play.

> Macbeth's desire for power makes him easily influenced. When he gets power, he is so desperate to keep it that he loses control of himself and his situation.

Now look at these four key points, taken from the same student's plan.

A
> Macbeth believes and acts on the witches' predictions

B
> Macbeth is driven by his ambition and the influence of Lady Macbeth

C
> Macbeth loses control as he grows desperate to keep his power

D
> Lady Macbeth seems powerful but loses control and self-control

One way to sequence the key points in a response is to work your way through the play **chronologically**, exploring how a character or theme develops as the play progresses.

(1) How would you sequence the four key points above if you were organising a response **chronologically**? Write ✐ the letters **A–D** in the order in which you would sequence them.

....

(2) Another way to organise the key points in a response is to **synthesise** your key points, by grouping related points together.

For example, you could:

(a) group your key points by **character**.

How would you sequence the key points above if you were going to explore power and control first in one character and then in another? ✐

....

Or you could:

(b) group your key points by **approach**.

How would you sequence the key points above if you were going to look at one way in which Shakespeare explores power and control, and then another way in which Shakespeare explores power and control? ✐

....

(3) Look at all of your answers above.

(a) Which method would **you** use to sequence the key points above? Tick ✓ it.

(b) Write ✐ **one** or **two** sentences explaining your choice.

....

....

Planning to write about the whole play

To plan an effective response, you need to:

- make a critical judgement summing up your response to the focus of the question
- gather relevant points: identify the key moments in the play that support your critical judgement and use them to develop points you can make in your response
- sequence your points: decide on the most effective way to build a logical argument that supports your critical judgement – for example, chronologically, by character, or by approach.

Look again at the exam-style question you saw at the start of the unit.

Exam-style question

In this extract Macbeth has lost control of himself and the situation.

Explain the importance of power and control elsewhere in the play.

Now look at these two paragraphs, written by a student in response to the exam-style question above.

> In Act 1, Shakespeare shows how King Duncan uses his power. He rewards Macbeth and Banquo for their victory in battle, and punishes the Thane of Cawdor's treachery with death. Ironically Duncan gives the title of Thane of Cawdor to Macbeth who is already plotting to take Duncan's power and become king himself. Although Duncan is not a very good judge of character, he does seem fair, punishing traitors and rewarding his loyal subjects, even if they only appear to be loyal.
>
> Macbeth, however, behaves very differently when he takes power and becomes king. He does not make his own decisions but is controlled and manipulated by the witches. He believes their predictions that he does not need to fear any man who is 'born of woman', and need have no fear at all until Birnam Wood moves. It is his failure to question these predictions that leads Macbeth to make foolish decisions that then lead to his death.

(1) Which of these critical judgements do these paragraphs support? Tick ✓ **one or more**:

A Shakespeare explores how destructive the desire for power can be. ☐

B Shakespeare shows the difference between a king who uses his power well and a king who uses it badly. ☐

C Shakespeare shows that you must have power over yourself before you can have power over others. ☐

(2) How has this student organised their key points? Tick ✓ **one**.

A chronologically ☐   B by character ☐   C by approach ☐

Your turn!

You are now going to **write your response** to the **second part** of the exam-style question.

Exam-style question

b In this extract Macbeth has lost control of himself and the situation.

Explain the importance of power and control elsewhere in the play.

In your answer you must consider:

• how power is shown

• how power affects characters in the play.

You should refer to the context of the play in your answer.   **(20 marks)**

1 Sum up ✐ your **critical judgement** in response to this exam-style question. This will be the **conclusion** that your response must support.

....

....

....

2 Which **key events or scenes** in the play will you explore in your response to support your critical judgement? Note ✐ them below.

3 Note ✐ down all the **key points** you will make to support your critical judgement.

....

....

....

....

....

....

4 **a** How will you sequence your key points? Tick ✓ one answer.

☐ chronologically   ☐ by character   ☐ by approach

b Number ✐ your key points in **3**, sequencing them to build an argument that supports your critical judgement.

5 Now write ✐ your response to the exam-style question above on paper.

Review your skills

Check up

Review your response to the exam-style question on page 47. Tick ✓ the column to show how well you think you have done each of the following.

	Not quite ✓	Nearly there ✓	Got it! ✓
Made a critical judgement	☐	☐	☐
Made key points using key scenes and events in the play to support my critical judgement	☐	☐	☐
Sequenced my key points to build an argument that supports my critical judgement	☐	☐	☐

Look over all of your work in this unit. Note 🖉 down the **three** most important things to remember when planning to write about the whole play.

1. ....

2. ....

3. ....

Need more practice?

Here is another exam-style question, relating to the extract from Act 4 Scene 3 of *Macbeth* on page 76 (Extract D).

Exam-style question

b This extract shows Macduff's reaction to violence and death.

Explain the importance of violence and death elsewhere in the play.

In your answer you must consider:
- how violence and death are shown
- how violence and death affect those involved.

You should refer to the context of the play in your answer. **(20 marks)**

Plan 🖉 your response to this question. You'll find some suggested ideas in the Answers section.

> Aim to: sum up your critical judgement in one or two sentences; identify key events to focus on, and key points to make; sequence your ideas.

How confident do you feel about each of these **skills?** Colour 🖉 in the bars.

1 How do I make a critical judgement? ☐☐☐☐

2 How do I gather relevant points? ☐☐☐☐

3 How do I sequence my points? ☐☐☐☐

⑦ Writing about the whole play

This unit will help you to write your response to the second part of the exam question. The skills you will build are to:

- know key events you can use when writing about the whole play
- understand how to use key events as evidence
- be able to analyse evidence from the play effectively.

> **Reminder:** For more help on writing about **the extract**, see units 2 and 3.

In the exam you will face questions like the ones below. This is about the extract on the next page. At the end of the unit you will **write your own response** to the **second part** of this question.

Exam-style question

a Explore how Shakespeare presents the relationship between Macbeth and the witches in this extract.

Refer closely to the extract in your answer. **(20 marks)**

b This extract shows the witches' predictions.

Explain the importance of predictions elsewhere in the play.

In your answer you must consider:

- how predictions are shown
- why predictions are important.

You should refer to the context of the play in your answer. **(20 marks)**

Before you tackle the question you will work through three key questions in the **skills boosts** to help you write your response.

① How do I choose key points in the play to focus on?

② How do I use evidence to support my ideas?

③ How do I analyse my evidence?

Read the extract on the next page from Act 4 Scene 1 of *Macbeth*.

As you read, think about the following:

↘ ↓ ↘

| What has happened before this scene? What happens after this scene? ☐ | How does Shakespeare present the witches in this extract? ☐ | How does Shakespeare present Macbeth's thoughts and feelings in this extract? ☐ |

Exam-style question

In this extract, Macbeth hears three predictions made by three apparitions conjured by the witches.

Extract A | Act 4 Scene 1 of *Macbeth*

Thunder. First Apparition: an armed Head
MACBETH
Tell me, thou unknown power,--
First Witch
He knows thy thought:
Hear his speech, but say thou nought.
First Apparition
Macbeth! Macbeth! Macbeth! beware Macduff;
5   Beware the Thane of Fife. Dismiss me. Enough.
Descends
MACBETH
Whate'er thou art, for thy good caution, thanks;
Thou hast harp'd my fear aright: but one word more,--
First Witch
He will not be commanded: here's another,
More potent than the first.
Thunder. Second Apparition: a bloody Child
Second Apparition
10   Macbeth! Macbeth! Macbeth!
MACBETH
Had I three ears, I'd hear thee.
Second Apparition
Be bloody, bold, and resolute; laugh to scorn
The power of man, for none of woman born
Shall harm Macbeth.
Descends
MACBETH
15   Then live, Macduff: what need I fear of thee?
But yet I'll make assurance double sure,
And take a bond of fate: thou shalt not live;
That I may tell pale-hearted fear it lies,
And sleep in spite of thunder.
Thunder. Third Apparition: a Child crowned, with a tree in his hand
20   What is this
That rises like the issue of a king,
And wears upon his baby-brow the round
And top of sovereignty?
ALL
Listen, but speak not to't.
Third Apparition
25   Be lion-mettled, proud; and take no care
Who chafes, who frets, or where conspirers are:
Macbeth shall never vanquish'd be until
Great Birnam wood to high Dunsinane hill
Shall come against him.
Descends
MACBETH
30   That will never be.
Who can impress the forest, bid the tree
Unfix his earth-bound root? Sweet bodements! good!

How do I choose key points in the play to focus on?

When you write about the extract, you should support your response with quotations from the extract. When you write about elsewhere in the play, you should refer to key events and scenes.

Reminder: For more help on writing about **the extract**, see units 2 and 3.

The key events in the play are those which:

- show a significant aspect of a key character
- explore a key theme
- are significant to the plot – the play would not develop in the same way without them.

(1) Look at the extract from Act 4 Scene 1 on page 50. Then either **add** (✐) or **delete** (c̶a̶t̶) words from the sentences below to explain the significance of this moment in the play.

> This moment in the play shows that Macbeth is easily influenced by the witches, still feeling guilty about the murders of Duncan and Banquo but ruthless in his determination to hold on to power.

> The themes of the supernatural, guilt, power and deception are all relevant to this moment.

(2) Now look at some of these other events in Act 3 and Act 4.

3.1 Banquo suspects Macbeth has 'play'd most foully'. He is going out riding. Macbeth persuades two murderers to kill Banquo and his son, Fleance. ☐	**3.2** Lady Macbeth is anxious about the murder of Duncan. Macbeth is anxious that Banquo is still alive. ☐
3.3 Banquo is murdered. Fleance escapes. ☐	**3.4** The ghost of Banquo appears at a banquet celebrating Macbeth becoming king. ☐
3.5 The witches know Macbeth will visit them again. ☐	**3.6** Lennox and a Lord discuss the deaths of Banquo and Duncan. ☐
4.2 Macbeth has Macduff's wife and child murdered. ☐	**4.3** Macduff learns that his family have been murdered. Malcolm and Macduff resolve to fight with the English army to defeat Macbeth. ☐

a) Which scenes reveal something about a key character? Label (✐) them with that character's name and **one** or **two** words to describe how that character is presented at this point in the play.

b) Which explore a key theme? Label (✐) them with the name of the key theme.

c) Which are significant to the plot? Label (✐) them **'plot'**.

d) Which key scenes and events in Acts 3 and 4 should you make sure you know? Tick (✓) them.

② How do I use evidence to support my ideas?

You can use **key events** in the play to **support** and **explain** your ideas about the play.

① Before you gather your ideas and evidence, you need to make a **critical judgement**. Write 🖉 **one** or **two** sentences summing up your critical judgement in response to this exam-style question.

Exam-style question

Explain the importance of predictions elsewhere in the play.

....

....

② Now think about **key events** elsewhere in the play. Which would support your critical judgement above? Tick ✓ any that you could use as evidence.

A	Macbeth and Banquo meet the witches	☐	E	Macbeth has Banquo murdered	☐
B	Macbeth is made Thane of Cawdor	☐	F	Macbeth has Macduff's family murdered	☐
C	Lady Macbeth persuades Macbeth to kill Duncan	☐	G	Lady Macbeth sleepwalks	☐
D	Macbeth kills Duncan	☐	H	Macbeth is killed by Macduff	☐

③ You now need to think in more detail about what happens at each of these key moments in the play.

A	Macbeth and Banquo meet the witches	**a** The witches tell Macbeth that he will be Thane of Cawdor and King of Scotland.
		b The witches tell Banquo that his descendants will be kings.

B	Macbeth is made Thane of Cawdor	**a** Ross and Angus tell Macbeth that the Thane of Cawdor is a traitor and will be executed.
		b Ross and Angus tell Macbeth that he has been given the title of Thane of Cawdor.

D	Macbeth kills Duncan	**a** Macbeth thinks he could murder Duncan and become king.
		b Macbeth is persuaded by Lady Macbeth to kill Duncan.
		c Macbeth forces himself to kill Duncan.
		d Macbeth is filled with guilt for killing Duncan.

a Which of these details support your critical judgement above? Draw lines 🖉 to link each key event with the most relevant detail(s).

b Review the evidence you have gathered. Use it to rewrite 🖉 or develop your critical judgement on paper.

3 How do I analyse my evidence?

Every key **idea or point** you make should be supported by **evidence** which you can **analyse**, exploring what it suggests about theme and character, and its impact on the audience.

Look at one student's key idea, or **critical judgement**, on the **importance of predictions** in *Macbeth*.

> Macbeth believes the witches' predictions

Now look at a **key event** you could use as evidence to support this idea.

> Macbeth is made Thane of Cawdor

To develop an effective analysis, you can consider these **four areas**.

Explain the evidence in the context of the play: Why does this support the key idea?	The witches predicted Macbeth would be Thane of Cawdor just before Macbeth learns that the prediction has come true.	☐
Think about character: What does this suggest about Macbeth's character?	This suggests that Macbeth is right to believe in the power of the witches' predictions and so it is not surprising that he believes their other prediction that he will become king.	☐
Think about theme: What does this suggest about the importance of predictions?	The witches' predictions are perhaps the biggest influence on Macbeth's decisions and actions in the play.	☐
Think about Shakespeare's intention: How does Shakespeare want the audience to respond at this point in the play?	Shakespeare uses this news to disturb the audience, as it confirms that the witches have the power of prediction and the power to influence Macbeth's choices.	☐

(1) Look at the student's ideas for analysis of the key event above. Which ideas would you include in your analysis of this evidence? Tick ✓ them.

Now look at another key event you could use as evidence to support the key idea above.

> Macbeth has Macduff's family murdered

(2) Use the **four areas of analysis** above to help you note 🖉 some ideas you could use in your analysis of this key event.

....

....

....

....

....

Writing about the whole play

To write an effective response, you should:

- be familiar with the key events of the play
- use key events as evidence to support your ideas about the play's key themes and characters
- analyse your evidence, thinking about theme, character and Shakespeare's intention.

Look again at the **second part** of the exam-style question you saw at the start of the unit.

Exam-style question

This extract shows the witches' predictions.

Explain the importance of predictions elsewhere in the play.

Now look at a paragraph taken from one student's response to the question.

Another consequence of the witches' predictions at the start of the play is Macbeth's decision to have Banquo murdered. The witches predicted that Banquo's descendants would become kings of Scotland and so Macbeth fears that Banquo and his son Fleance will challenge his power. This shows the influence of the witches' predictions on Macbeth's choices and decisions but also his heartless ruthlessness in acting on them. Banquo is Macbeth's friend and they fought together in the battle at the start of the play. This makes his murder even more shocking for the audience because the witches' predictions are influencing Macbeth to put power above friendship and loyalty.

- uses a key event as evidence
- explains the context of the evidence
- analysis comments on character
- analysis comments on theme
- analysis comments on Shakespeare's intention

① Can you identify all the different things the student has included in this paragraph? Link 🖉 the annotations to the paragraph to show where the student has included them.

Your turn!

You are now going to **write your own response** to the exam-style question below.

b This extract shows the witches' predictions.

Explain the importance of predictions elsewhere in the play.

In your answer you must consider:
- how predictions are shown
- why predictions are important

You should refer to the context of the play in your answer.   **(20 marks)**

1 Write 🖉 **one** or **two** sentences summarising your critical judgement in response to the question.

....

....

2 Which key events in the play would support your critical judgement? Write 🖉 them below.

3 Look at all the evidence you have gathered. Think about:
- what your evidence suggests about character
- what your evidence suggests about the theme you are exploring: the importance of predictions
- what your evidence suggests about Shakespeare's intention: how might the audience respond at this point?

Annotate 🖉 your evidence with your ideas.

4 Look at your annotated evidence.

a Which are your strongest ideas? Tick ✓ them.

b Number 🖉 the ideas you have ticked, sequencing them to build an argument that supports your critical judgement.

5 Now write 🖉 your response to the exam-style question above on paper.

Review your skills

Check up

Review your response to the exam-style question on page 55. Tick ✓ the column to show how well you think you have done each of the following.

	Not quite ✓	Nearly there ✓	Got it! ✓
selected relevant key events to support my critical judgement	☐	☐	☐
analysed my evidence effectively	☐	☐	☐

Look over all of your work in this unit. Note ✎ down the **three** most important things to remember when writing about the whole play.

1. ....

2. ....

3. ....

Need more practice?

Here is another exam-style question, relating to the extract from Act 4 Scene 3 of *Macbeth* on page 76 (Extract D).

Exam-style question

a Explore how Shakespeare presents Macduff's feelings in this extract.

Refer closely to the extract in your answer. **(20 marks)**

b This extract shows Macduff's reaction to violence and death.

Explain the importance of violence and death elsewhere in the play.

In your answer you must consider:
• how violence and death are shown
• how violence and death affect those involved.

You should refer to the context of the play in your answer. **(20 marks)**

Write ✎ your response to the **second part** of this question. You'll find some suggested ideas in the Answers section.

How confident do you feel about each of these SKills? Colour ✎ in the bars.

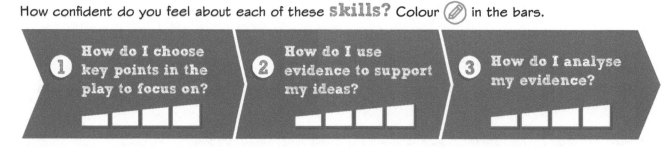

1 How do I choose key points in the play to focus on?
☐☐☐☐

2 How do I use evidence to support my ideas?
☐☐☐☐

3 How do I analyse my evidence?
☐☐☐☐

⑧ Commenting on context

This unit will help you to show your understanding of the play's context: its relationship with the time the play was written and first performed. The skills you will build are to:

- understand the relationship between the play and its context
- explain the impact of context on different elements of the play
- incorporate comments on context into your writing about the play.

In the exam you will face questions like the ones below. This is about the extract on the next page. At the end of the unit you will **write your own response** to the **second part** of this question.

Exam-style question

a Explore how Shakespeare presents Lady Macbeth in this extract.

Refer closely to the extract in your answer. **(20 marks)**

b This extract shows Lady Macbeth troubled by her conscience.

Explain the importance of conscience elsewhere in the play.

In your answer you must consider:

- how conscience is shown
- how conscience affects those who show it.

You should refer to the context of the play in your answer. **(20 marks)**

Before you tackle the question you will work through three key questions in the **skills boosts** to help you write about the play's context.

1 How do I know which contextual ideas to write about?

2 How do I comment on context?

3 How do I build my comments on context into my analysis?

Read the extract on the next page from Act 5 Scene 1 of *Macbeth*.

As you read, think about the following: ✓

What has happened before this scene? What happens after this scene?

How does Shakespeare present Lady Macbeth in this extract?

How does Shakespeare show her thoughts and feelings in this extract?

Exam-style question

In this extract, Lady Macbeth is sleepwalking, watched by her doctor and a gentlewoman.

Extract A | Act 5 Scene 1 of *Macbeth*

Doctor
What is it she does now? Look, how she rubs her hands.
Gentlewoman
It is an accustomed action with her, to seem thus
washing her hands: I have known her continue in
this a quarter of an hour.
LADY MACBETH
5   Yet here's a spot.
Doctor
Hark! she speaks: I will set down what comes from
her, to satisfy my remembrance the more strongly.
LADY MACBETH
Out, damned spot! out, I say!--One: two: why,
then, 'tis time to do't.--Hell is murky!--Fie, my
10   lord, fie! a soldier, and afeard? What need we
fear who knows it, when none can call our power to
account?--Yet who would have thought the old man
to have had so much blood in him.
Doctor
Do you mark that?
LADY MACBETH
15   The Thane of Fife had a wife: where is she now?--
What, will these hands ne'er be clean?--No more o'
that, my lord, no more o' that: you mar all with
this starting.
Doctor
Go to, go to; you have known what you should not.
Gentlewoman
20   She has spoke what she should not, I am sure of
that: heaven knows what she has known.
LADY MACBETH
Here's the smell of the blood still: all the
perfumes of Arabia will not sweeten this little
hand. Oh, oh, oh!
Doctor
25   What a sigh is there! The heart is sorely charged.
Gentlewoman
I would not have such a heart in my bosom for the
dignity of the whole body.

1 How do I know which contextual ideas to write about?

You need to be aware of all the different contexts of *Macbeth* on which you could comment so that you can choose those that are relevant to your response.

1 Look at some of the features of *Macbeth* and the time in which it was written. Tick ✓ any that are relevant to the play, and cross ✕ any that are not.

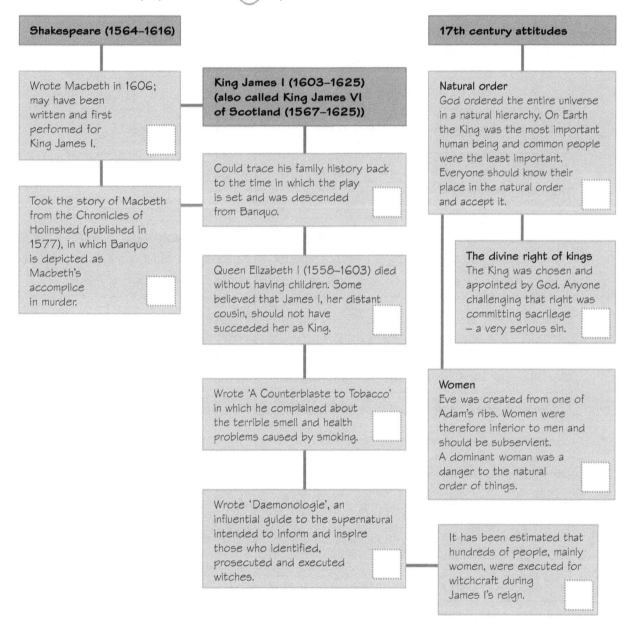

Shakespeare (1564–1616)

Wrote Macbeth in 1606; may have been written and first performed for King James I. ☐

Took the story of Macbeth from the Chronicles of Holinshed (published in 1577), in which Banquo is depicted as Macbeth's accomplice in murder. ☐

King James I (1603–1625) (also called King James VI of Scotland (1567–1625))

Could trace his family history back to the time in which the play is set and was descended from Banquo. ☐

Queen Elizabeth I (1558–1603) died without having children. Some believed that James I, her distant cousin, should not have succeeded her as King. ☐

Wrote 'A Counterblaste to Tobacco' in which he complained about the terrible smell and health problems caused by smoking. ☐

Wrote 'Daemonologie', an influential guide to the supernatural intended to inform and inspire those who identified, prosecuted and executed witches. ☐

17th century attitudes

Natural order
God ordered the entire universe in a natural hierarchy. On Earth the King was the most important human being and common people were the least important. Everyone should know their place in the natural order and accept it. ☐

The divine right of kings
The King was chosen and appointed by God. Anyone challenging that right was committing sacrilege – a very serious sin. ☐

Women
Eve was created from one of Adam's ribs. Women were therefore inferior to men and should be subservient. A dominant woman was a danger to the natural order of things. ☐

It has been estimated that hundreds of people, mainly women, were executed for witchcraft during James I's reign. ☐

2 Now think about some of these key events and characters in the play.

| Macbeth | Lady Macbeth | The witches | Murder of Duncan |

Annotate ✎ the diagram with these words, using arrows ⬇ to link them to all the relevant elements of context.

2 How do I comment on context?

An effective comment on the context of *Macbeth* should focus on **when** the play was written, a **relevant belief, attitude or situation** at that time, the impact that Shakespeare intended to have on his audience and, perhaps, how a modern audience's response could differ.

Look at the beginning of one student's paragraph exploring how Lady Macbeth is presented in Act 1 Scene 5.

> Lady Macbeth calls upon 'spirits' to fill her with 'direst cruelty', which suggests she is trying to use the power of witchcraft to achieve her ambitions.

① Now look at some different students' comments on the context of the play in this scene.

A | Lady Macbeth is like a witch because people believed in them in those days. |

B | Shakespeare uses his seventeenth-century audience's fear of witchcraft to make Lady Macbeth a terrifying character. |

C | To a twenty-first-century audience, Lady Macbeth seems cruel, powerful and manipulative, but to a seventeenth-century audience she would be much more disturbing: a witch threatening the power of the men around her and the natural order of things. |

a Which comment does what? Circle Ⓐ or cross out ~~cat~~ each letter in the table below.

Context	Comment		
identifies the time in which the play was written	A	B	C
identifies a relevant belief, attitude or situation at that time	A	B	C
considers Shakespeare's intention	A	B	C
considers the impact on an audience	A	B	C
compares today's audience with Shakespeare's audience	A	B	C

b Which of the comments above would you use when writing about Lady Macbeth in Act 1 Scene 5? Tick ✓ one or more.

② Look at these sentences from the beginning of another student's paragraph about the witches.

> The play begins with a very short scene featuring the witches. It does not help to tell the story of 'Macbeth' but is very dramatic and engaging.

a Write ✎ a sentence or two adding a contextual comment to the paragraph.

Why would this scene be so dramatic and engaging for Shakespeare's audience?

....

....

b Check your comment. Does it achieve all or most of the criteria listed in question ①a?

Circle Ⓐ   Yes / No

3 How do I build my comments on context into my analysis?

You do not need to make contextual comments in every paragraph of your response, but you do need to make them relevant to your analysis of the play.

Look at the opening of a paragraph from a student's response, commenting on the presentation of Lady Macbeth in Act 1 Scene 7.

> In Act 1 Scene 7, Lady Macbeth tries to persuade her husband to keep his promise to kill King Duncan. She tells him that she would have 'dash'd' her baby's brains out if she had promised to do so.

(1) Now look at some sentences you could add to this paragraph.

A This violent, graphic example shows how desperate she is to influence Macbeth and achieve her own ambitions.

a To Shakespeare's audience she would appear even more powerful and Macbeth would seem even weaker.

B This hideous image shows her cruelty and cold-heartedness. She would do anything to get her own way.

b This makes her sound like a witch because the witches talk about murder and cold-hearted cruelty so it makes her more frightening because Shakespeare's audience would have been frightened of witches.

C This disturbing image reveals her impatience with Macbeth's failure to make a decision and act like a man.

c Shakespeare's audience were worried about challenges to power because of the Gunpowder Plot and other threats to King James I and so they would have been disturbed by Lady Macbeth's challenge to Macbeth's power.

D In showing her strength, she is challenging Macbeth's manliness and highlighting his weakness.

d This challenge to her husband would have shocked a seventeenth-century audience who expected women to be obedient and respectful to their husbands.

a Which sentence(s):
- comment on the impact of the evidence in the paragraph above? Label 🖉 them 'impact'.
- comment on the play's context? Label 🖉 them 'context'.

b Which comments about context are relevant to which comments about impact? Draw 🖉 lines linking them.

c Which of the sentences above would you include in a paragraph analysing how Shakespeare presents Lady Macbeth in Act 1 Scene 7 and how would you sequence them? Number 🖉 your chosen sentences.

Commenting on context

To comment effectively on context, you need to:

- use a relevant contextual point to develop your analysis of a key point, supported with evidence
- explore what this contextual idea adds to your understanding of Shakespeare's intention and his audience's response.

Look again at this exam-style question you saw at the start of the unit.

Exam-style question

This extract shows Lady Macbeth troubled by her conscience.
Explain the importance of conscience elsewhere in the play.

In your answer you must consider:

- how conscience is shown
- how conscience affects those who show it

You should refer to the context of the play in your answer. **(20 marks)**

Now look at a paragraph focusing on the play as a whole, taken from one student's response to the question.

When Lady Macbeth reads Macbeth's letter about the witches' predictions, she calls on the forces of evil to 'unsex' her and fill her with 'direst cruelty' so that she has the power to persuade her husband to murder Duncan. This is a disturbing moment in the play for a modern audience as it suggests she is trying to overcome her conscience so that she can persuade Macbeth to commit murder. However, because Shakespeare's audience firmly believed in 'spirits' and witches and the harm that they could do to normal human beings, this would be a terrifying moment for them. Shakespeare wants his audience to be both shocked and disturbed by Lady Macbeth and even more so because this is her first appearance in the play.

- uses a key event as evidence
- uses a quotation as evidence
- comments on the impact of the evidence
- identifies a relevant contextual point
- explores Shakespeare's intention in the light of this contextual point
- explores the audience's response in the light of this contextual point

(1) Can you identify all the different things the student has included in this paragraph? Link ✐ the annotations to the paragraph to show where the student has included them.

Your turn!

You are now going to **write your own answer** in response to the **second part** of the exam-style question.

> ### Exam-style question
>
> **b** This extract shows Lady Macbeth troubled by her conscience.
> Explain the importance of conscience elsewhere in the play.
>
> In your answer you must consider:
>
> - how conscience is shown
> - how conscience affects those who show it
>
> You should refer to the context of the play in your answer. **(20 marks)**

① Write ✏ **one** or **two** sentences, summarising your critical judgement in response to the question.

....

....

② Which key events in the play would support your critical judgement? Note ✏ them below.

③ Look at all the evidence you have gathered. Think about:
- what your evidence suggests about conscience
- what your evidence suggests about Shakespeare's intention: how might the audience respond at this point?

Annotate ✏ your evidence with your ideas.

④ Now think about the relevant contextual points you could make in your response. Annotate ✏ your evidence with your ideas.

⑤ Look at your annotated evidence.

  a Which are your strongest ideas? Tick ✓ them.

  b Number ✏ the ideas that you have ticked to show how you would sequence them to build an argument that supports your critical judgement.

⑥ Now write ✏ your response to the exam-style question above on paper.

Review your skills

Check up

Review your response to the exam-style question on page 63. Tick ✓ the column to show how well you think you have done each of the following.

	Not quite ✓	Nearly there ✓	Got it! ✓
identified relevant contextual points	☐	☐	☐
used relevant contextual points to develop my analysis	☐	☐	☐
explored Shakespeare's intention and the audience's response in the light of the play's context	☐	☐	☐

Look over all of your work in this unit. Note ✐ down the **three** most important things to remember when commenting on context.

1. ....

2. ....

3. ....

Need more practice?

Here is another exam-style question, this time relating to the extract from Act 5 Scene 3 on page 77 (Extract E).

Exam-style question

a Explore how Shakespeare presents Macbeth's thoughts and feelings in this extract.
   Refer closely to the extract in your answer. **(20 marks)**

b This extract shows Macbeth talking about fear.
   Explain the importance of fear elsewhere in the play.
   In your answer you must consider:
   • how fear is shown
   • how fear affects those who experience it
   You should refer to the context of the play in your answer. **(20 marks)**

Write ✐ your response to the **second part** of this question. You'll find some suggested points to refer to in the Answers section.

How confident do you feel about each of these **skills**? Colour ✐ in the bars.

1 How do I know which contextual ideas to write about?

2 How do I comment on context?

3 How do I build my comments on context into my analysis?

⑨ Developing a critical writing style

This unit will help you to express your ideas about Macbeth as clearly and precisely as possible. The skills you will build are to:

- select vocabulary to express your ideas precisely
- link your ideas to express them clearly
- extend your sentences to develop ideas more fully.

In the exam you will face questions like the one below. This is about the extract on the next page. At the end of the unit you will **write one paragraph** in response to the **second part** of this question.

> **Exam-style question**
>
> **a** Explore how Shakespeare presents the character of Macbeth in this extract.
>
>   Refer closely to the extract in your answer. **(20 marks)**
>
> **b** This extract shows the result of Macbeth's choices and decisions in the play.
>
>   Explain the importance of making choices elsewhere in the play.
>
>   In your answer you must consider:
>   - how choices are shown
>   - the reasons for those choices.
>
>   You should refer to the context of the play in your answer. **(20 marks)**

Before you tackle the question you will work through three key questions in the **skills boosts** to help you develop a critical writing style.

① How do I choose vocabulary which expresses my ideas precisely?

② How can I link my ideas to express them more clearly?

③ How can I extend my sentences to develop my ideas more fully?

Read the extract on the next page from Act 5 Scene 8 of *Macbeth*.

As you read, think about the following: ⊘

What has happened before this scene? What happens after this scene?	Why does Macbeth choose to fight Macduff?	How have Macbeth's choices brought him to this situation?
☐	☐	☐

In this extract, Macbeth fights Macduff.

Extract A | Act 5 Scene 8 of *Macbeth*

MACDUFF
Turn, hell-hound, turn!
MACBETH
Of all men else I have avoided thee:
But get thee back; my soul is too much charged
With blood of thine already.
MACDUFF
5   I have no words:
My voice is in my sword: thou bloodier villain
Than terms can give thee out!
They fight
MACBETH
Thou losest labour:
As easy mayst thou the intrenchant air
10   With thy keen sword impress as make me bleed:
Let fall thy blade on vulnerable crests;
I bear a charmed life, which must not yield
To one of woman born.
MACDUFF
Despair thy charm;
15   And let the angel whom thou still hast served
Tell thee, Macduff was from his mother's womb
Untimely ripp'd.
MACBETH
Accursed be that tongue that tells me so,
For it hath cow'd my better part of man!
20   And be these juggling fiends no more believed,
That palter with us in a double sense;
That keep the word of promise to our ear,
And break it to our hope. I'll not fight with thee.
MACDUFF
Then yield thee, coward,
25   And live to be the show and gaze o' the time:
We'll have thee, as our rarer monsters are,
Painted on a pole, and underwrit,
'Here may you see the tyrant.'
MACBETH
I will not yield,
30   To kiss the ground before young Malcolm's feet,
And to be baited with the rabble's curse.
Though Birnam wood be come to Dunsinane,
And thou opposed, being of no woman born,
Yet I will try the last. Before my body
35   I throw my warlike shield. Lay on, Macduff,
And damn'd be him that first cries, 'Hold, enough!'

1 How do I choose vocabulary which expresses my ideas precisely?

You need to choose precise vocabulary to describe your response to the play as fully and accurately as possible.

How you would describe Shakespeare's presentation of these key characters at each of these points in the play?

Macbeth	
1.7 tries to halt the plan to kill Duncan	
1.7 is persuaded to kill Duncan	
2.1 expresses doubts about killing Duncan	
2.2 kills Duncan	
2.2 is filled with guilt and remorse for killing Duncan	
4.2 has Macduff's family killed	
Lady Macbeth	
1.5 calls upon 'spirits' to fill her with cruelty	
1.5 persuades her husband to murder Duncan	
1.7 questions Macbeth's masculinity	
2.2 has drunk alcohol to make her 'bold'	
2.2 returns the blood-stained daggers to Duncan's chamber	
5.1 sleepwalks	

1. Choose **two** words from the list below and write ✏ them in the table above next to the relevant point in the play. Aim to choose words that describe your response as precisely as possible. Choose words with a similar meaning, or two very different words expressing different possible responses.

desperate	persuasive	brave	worried	cowardly	insincere
cruel	manipulative	decisive	unstable	fearful	deceitful
ambitious	cunning	devoted	troubled	vulnerable	hypocritical
ruthless	powerful	loyal	disturbed	submissive	duplicitous
evil	dominant	strong	mad	impotent	delusional

2. Now think about Shakespeare's intention: how did he want the audience to respond to these characters at these points in the play? Choose **one or two** of the words below and add ✏ them to the relevant points in the play in question 1.

excitement	disappointment	revulsion	fear	admiration
anticipation	relief	disgust	shock	sorrow
tension	concern	anger	confusion	sympathy

2 How can I link my ideas to express them more clearly?

You can use conjunctions to link your ideas, helping you to express your ideas more clearly and fluently.

Coordinating conjunctions link related or contrasting ideas:	Subordinating conjunctions express more complex connections:
and but or so	• an explanation, e.g. because in order to
	• a comparison, e.g. although whereas
	• a sequence, e.g. when after until

① Look at these pairs of sentences.

A

☐ Macbeth meets the witches. They make three predictions.

☐ Macbeth is unsure about murdering Duncan. Lady Macbeth has no doubts at all.

☐ Macbeth feels some loyalty to Duncan. He has just made him Thane of Cawdor.

B

☐ When Macbeth meets the witches, they make three predictions.

☐ Macbeth is unsure about murdering Duncan whereas Lady Macbeth has no doubts at all.

☐ Macbeth feels some loyalty to Duncan because he has just made him Thane of Cawdor.

a Circle Ⓐ the conjunctions in the sentences labelled **B**.

b Tick ✓ the version of each sentence that you feel is most clearly and fluently expressed.

② Rewrite ✎ these pairs of sentences, using a conjunction to link them. Remember to choose and position your conjunction carefully to express each idea as clearly and fluently as possible.

Lady Macbeth receives a letter from Macbeth. ✚ She calls upon 'spirits' to fill her with cruelty.

....

....

Lady Macbeth is manipulative. ✚ Macbeth makes the decision to murder Duncan.

....

....

Macbeth feels guilt at the murder of Duncan. ✚ He shows none at the killing of Macduff's family.

....

....

3 How can I extend my sentences to develop my ideas more fully?

One way to extend your sentences, and develop your ideas, is by using conjunctions. Other ways include:
- using present participles: a verb ending in –ing
- using the pronoun which.

Conjunctions						
and	but	when	as	before	after	
although	if	whereas	unless	because	since	

This sentence could be completed:

> Macbeth chooses to visit the witches...

- using this conjunction:
  > (after) the disturbing appearance of Banquo's ghost.

- or a different conjunction:
  > (in order to) discover his fate.

- or a present participle:
  > (believing) that they will reveal his fate.

- or which:
  > (which) results in his mistaken belief that he is invincible.

(1) Complete ✏ this sentence in four different ways.   > Macbeth believes the witches' predictions

   a Use a conjunction: ....

   b Use a different conjunction: ....

   c Use which: ....

   d Use a present participle: ....

You can use 'which' or a present participle to avoid repeatedly beginning sentences with 'This suggests...' or 'This shows...'. For example:

> Macbeth is easily persuaded. (This suggests) he is weak.

> Macbeth is easily persuaded (which suggests) he is weak.

> Macbeth is easily persuaded, (suggesting) he is weak.

(2) Change ✏ these sentences to make them a single sentence, using a present participle or 'which'.

   a > Lady Macbeth seems to have total control. <u>This encourages</u> the audience to see Macbeth as powerless.

   b > Macbeth chooses to murder Banquo without Lady Macbeth's influence. <u>This creates</u> the impression that he is becoming more independent and more ruthless.

(3) Re-read all the sentences you have written on this page to check that they are fluently and clearly expressed. On paper, re-write ✏ any that are not.

Developing a critical writing style

To express your ideas clearly and precisely, you can:
- select vocabulary that expresses your ideas precisely
- link your ideas using conjunctions, present participles, etc, to develop and express them clearly.

Look again at this exam style question you saw at the start of the unit.

Exam-style question

b This extract shows the result of Macbeth's choices and decisions in the play.

Explain the importance of making choices elsewhere in the play.

In your answer you must consider:
- how choices are shown
- the reasons for those choices.

You should refer to the context of the play in your answer.   (20 marks)

(1) Look at a short paragraph from one student's response to the question.

> At the start of the play Macbeth is presented as good and strong. He fights successfully in battle for King Duncan. He is described as 'brave'. He goes home to Lady Macbeth. She starts telling him to murder Duncan. This suggests that it is Lady Macbeth who makes her husband make bad choices. It gives the impression that Macbeth is good but weak.

a Underline (A) **at least three** examples of vocabulary which could be more precise.

b Note (✎) down in the margin **at least three** alternative vocabulary choices for each one.

c Mark (✎) any of the sentences which you feel should be linked or developed to improve the clarity and precision of the writing.

d Write (✎) an improved version of this paragraph, either by adjusting the text above or by re-writing (✎) it in the space below.

....

....

....

....

....

Your turn!

You are now going to **write one paragraph** in response to the **second part** of the exam-style question.

Exam-style question

b This extract shows the result of Macbeth's choices and decisions in the play.

Explain the importance of making choices elsewhere in the play.

In your answer you must consider:
• how choices are shown
• the reasons for those choices.

You should refer to the context of the play in your answer.   (20 marks)

1   **a**   Think about some of the choices made in the play. Tick ✓ whether you think they are a good choice, bad choice or whether there was no choice.

	Good choice?	Bad choice?	No choice?
• Macbeth is made Thane of Cawdor	☐	☐	☐
• Macbeth murders Duncan	☐	☐	☐
• Lady Macbeth persuades Macbeth to murder Duncan	☐	☐	☐
• Macbeth has Banquo killed	☐	☐	☐
• Macbeth decides to visit the witches	☐	☐	☐
• Macbeth believes the witches' second three predictions	☐	☐	☐
• Macbeth has Macduff's family murdered.	☐	☐	☐

b   Choose **one or two** of the key events from the play which you can explore in your response to the exam-style question. You could choose from the list above, or use your own ideas. Note 🖉 them below.

....

....

....

....

....

c   Look at each of your chosen key events. How is each choice shown? Why was that choice made? What impression does it create of the character who makes it? How has Shakespeare created that impression? Add 🖉 your ideas to your notes above.

d   Use your ideas to write 🖉 **one** paragraph on paper in response to the exam-style question.

Remember to:
• choose your vocabulary carefully
• think about ways in which you can link your ideas to develop and express them clearly and precisely.

Review your skills

Check up

Review your response to the exam-style question on page 71. Tick ✓ the column to show how well you think you have done each of the following.

	Not quite ✓	Nearly there ✓	Got it! ✓
selected precise vocabulary	☐	☐	☐
linked and developed my ideas clearly and precisely using conjunctions, present participles etc.	☐	☐	☐

Look over all of your work in this unit. Note 🖉 down the **three** most important things to remember when trying to express your ideas as clearly and precisely as possible.

1. ....

2. ....

3. ....

Need more practice?

You can EITHER:

(1) Look again at your paragraph written in response to the exam-style question on page 71. Re-write 🖉 it, experimenting with different vocabulary choices and sentence structures, linking your ideas in different ways. Which paragraph is most effective in expressing your ideas clearly and precisely?

AND/OR:

(2) Choose another point from the suggestions on page 71. Write 🖉 a further paragraph in response to the exam-style question, focusing closely on your vocabulary choices and sentence structures.

How confident do you feel about each of these skills? Colour 🖉 in the bars.

1 How do I choose vocabulary which expresses my ideas precisely?	2 How can I link my ideas to express them more clearly?	3 How can I extend my sentences to develop my ideas more fully?
☐☐☐☐	☐☐☐☐	☐☐☐☐

More practice questions

Units 1 and 2

Exam-style question

In this extract, a Captain has returned from the battlefield, and describes how Macbeth helped Duncan's army to win a great victory over the invading Norwegian army.

Extract A | Act 1 Scene 2 of *Macbeth*

MALCOLM
This is the sergeant
Who like a good and hardy soldier fought
'Gainst my captivity. Hail, brave friend!
Say to the king the knowledge of the broil
5   As thou didst leave it.
CAPTAIN
Doubtful it stood;
As two spent swimmers, that do cling together
And choke their art. The merciless Macdonwald–
Worthy to be a rebel, for to that
10   The multiplying villanies of nature
Do swarm upon him–from the western isles
Of kerns and gallowglasses is supplied;
And fortune, on his damned quarrel smiling,
Show'd like a rebel's whore. But all's too weak:
15   For brave Macbeth–well he deserves that name–
Disdaining fortune, with his brandish'd steel,
Which smoked with bloody execution,
Like valour's minion carved out his passage
Till he faced the slave;
20   Which ne'er shook hands, nor bade farewell to him,
Till he unseam'd him from the nave to the chops,
And fix'd his head upon our battlements.
DUNCAN
O valiant cousin! worthy gentleman!

a Explore how Shakespeare presents the character of Macbeth in this extract.

Refer closely to the extract in your answer.   **(20 marks)**

b This extract shows the violence of the battlefield.

Explain the importance of violence elsewhere in the play.

In your answer you must consider:

- how violence is shown

- the reasons for the violence.

You should refer to the context of the play in your answer.

                                                                                  (20 marks)

Unit 1 Note down ✏ the key events in the play you would choose to write about in your response to this question.

Unit 2 Write ✏ **one** or **two** paragraphs in response to the **first part** of this question.

Exam-style question

In this extract, Banquo reflects on his suspicions that Macbeth has murdered Duncan. Macbeth assures Banquo of his trust and friendship, while secretly planning to murder him.

Extract B | Act 3 Scene 1 of *Macbeth*

Enter BANQUO

BANQUO
Thou hast it now: king, Cawdor, Glamis, all,
As the weird women promised, and, I fear,
Thou play'dst most foully for't: yet it was said
It should not stand in thy posterity,
5   But that myself should be the root and father
Of many kings. If there come truth from them–
As upon thee, Macbeth, their speeches shine–
Why, by the verities on thee made good,
May they not be my oracles as well,
10 And set me up in hope? But hush! no more.

Sennet sounded. Enter MACBETH, as king, LADY MACBETH, as queen, LENNOX, ROSS, Lords, Ladies, and Attendants

MACBETH
Here's our chief guest.
LADY MACBETH
If he had been forgotten,
It had been as a gap in our great feast,
And all-thing unbecoming.
MACBETH
15 Tonight we hold a solemn supper sir,
And I'll request your presence.
BANQUO
Let your Highness
Command upon me; to the which my duties
Are with a most indissoluble tie
20 For ever knit.
MACBETH
Ride you this afternoon?
BANQUO
Ay, my good lord.
MACBETH
We should have else desired your good advice,
Which still hath been both grave and prosperous,
25 In this day's council; but we'll take tomorrow.

a Explore how Shakespeare presents the character of Banquo in this extract.

Refer closely to the extract in your answer. **(20 marks)**

b This extract shows dishonesty and deception.

Explain the importance of dishonesty and deception elsewhere in the play.

In your answer you must consider:

• how dishonesty and deception are shown

• the reasons for dishonesty and deception

You should refer to the context of the play in your answer. **(20 marks)**

Unit 3 Write **one** or **two** paragraphs in response to the **first part** of this question.

Exam-style question

In this extract, Macbeth and Lady Macbeth discuss their thoughts and feelings following the murder of King Duncan. They have invited all the Thanes of Scotland to a coronation banquet.

Extract C | Act 3 Scene 2 of *Macbeth*

LADY MACBETH
Nought's had, all's spent,
Where our desire is got without content:
'Tis safer to be that which we destroy
Than by destruction dwell in doubtful joy.
Enter MACBETH
5   How now, my lord! why do you keep alone,
Of sorriest fancies your companions making,
Using those thoughts which should indeed have died
With them they think on? Things without all remedy
Should be without regard: what's done is done.
MACBETH
10   We have scotch'd the snake, not kill'd it:
She'll close and be herself, whilst our poor malice
Remains in danger of her former tooth.
But let the frame of things disjoint, both the worlds suffer,
Ere we will eat our meal in fear and sleep
15   In the affliction of these terrible dreams
That shake us nightly: better be with the dead,
Whom we, to gain our peace, have sent to peace,
Than on the torture of the mind to lie
In restless ecstasy. Duncan is in his grave;
20   After life's fitful fever he sleeps well;
Treason has done his worst: nor steel, nor poison,
Malice domestic, foreign levy, nothing,
Can touch him further.
LADY MACBETH
Come on;
25   Gentle my lord, sleek o'er your rugged looks;
Be bright and jovial among your guests tonight.
MACBETH
So shall I, love; and so, I pray, be you:
Let your remembrance apply to Banquo;
Present him eminence, both with eye and tongue:
30   Unsafe the while, that we
Must lave our honours in these flattering streams,
And make our faces vizards to our hearts,
Disguising what they are.
LADY MACBETH
You must leave this.
MACBETH
35   O, full of scorpions is my mind, dear wife!
Thou know'st that Banquo, and his Fleance, lives.

a Explore how Shakespeare presents Macbeth's and Lady Macbeth's feelings in this extract.
    Refer closely to the extract in your answer.   **(20 marks)**

b This extract shows Lady Macbeth telling Macbeth to hide his true feelings and give the false
    appearance of being happy. Explain the importance of false appearances elsewhere in the play.
    In your answer you must consider:
    • how false appearances are shown
    • how false appearances affect those involved,
    You should refer to the context of the play in your answer.   **(20 marks)**

Unit 4 Write your response to the **first part** of this question.

Unit 5 Write your response to the **second part** of this question.

Exam-style question

In this extract, Macduff learns that Macbeth has had his family murdered.

Extract D | Act 4 Scene 3 of Macbeth

ROSS
Your castle is surprised; your wife and babes
Savagely slaughter'd: to relate the manner
Were, on the quarry of these murder'd deer,
To add the death of you.

MALCOLM
5 Merciful heaven!
What, man! Ne'er pull your hat upon your brows;
Give sorrow words: the grief that does not speak
Whispers the o'er-fraught heart and bids it break.

MACDUFF
My children too?

ROSS
10 Wife, children, servants, all
That could be found.

MACDUFF
And I must be from thence!
My wife kill'd too?

ROSS
I have said.

MALCOLM
15 Be comforted:
Let's make us medicines of our great revenge,
To cure this deadly grief.

MACDUFF
He has no children. All my pretty ones?
Did you say all? O hell-kite! All?
20 What, all my pretty chickens and their dam
At one fell swoop?

MALCOLM
Dispute it like a man.

MACDUFF
I shall do so;
But I must also feel it as a man:
25 I cannot but remember such things were,
That were most precious to me. Did heaven look on,
And would not take their part? Sinful Macduff,
They were all struck for thee! Naught that I am,
Not for their own demerits, but for mine,
30 Fell slaughter on their souls. Heaven rest them now!

MALCOLM
Be this the whetstone of your sword: let grief
Convert to anger; blunt not the heart, enrage it.

a Explore how Shakespeare presents Macduff's feelings in this extract.
Refer closely to the extract in your answer.   **(20 marks)**

b This extract shows Macduff's reaction to violence and death.
Explain the importance of violence and death elsewhere in the play.
In your answer you must consider:
• how violence and death are shown
• how violence and death affect those involved.
You should refer to the context of the play in your answer.   **(20 marks)**

Unit 6 Plan ✎ your response to the **second part** of this question.

Unit 7 Write ✎ your response to the **second part** of this question.

In this extract, Macbeth has learned that Malcolm and the English army are approaching, and that his Thanes have all deserted him. He calls for his loyal servant, Seyton.

Extract E | Act 5 Scene 3 of *Macbeth*

> **MACBETH**
> Bring me no more reports; let them fly all:
> Till Birnam wood remove to Dunsinane,
> I cannot taint with fear. What's the boy Malcolm?
> Was he not born of woman? The spirits that know
> 5   All mortal consequences have pronounced me thus:
> 'Fear not, Macbeth; no man that's born of woman
> Shall e'er have power upon thee.' Then fly, false thanes,
> And mingle with the English epicures:
> The mind I sway by and the heart I bear
> 10   Shall never sag with doubt nor shake with fear.
>
> *Enter a Servant*
>
> The devil damn thee black, thou cream-faced loon!
> Where got'st thou that goose look?
> **Servant**
> There is ten thousand–
> **MACBETH**
> Geese, villain?
> **Servant**
> 15   Soldiers, sir.
> **MACBETH**
> Go prick thy face, and over-red thy fear,
> Thou lily-liver'd boy. What soldiers, patch?
> Death of thy soul! those linen cheeks of thine
> Are counsellors to fear. What soldiers, whey-face?
> **Servant**
> 20   The English force, so please you.
> **MACBETH**
> Take thy face hence.
>
> *Exit Servant*
>
> Seyton!–I am sick at heart,
> When I behold–Seyton, I say!–This push
> Will cheer me ever, or disseat me now.
> 25   I have lived long enough: my way of life
> Is fall'n into the sear, the yellow leaf;
> And that which should accompany old age,
> As honour, love, obedience, troops of friends,
> I must not look to have; but, in their stead,
> 30   Curses, not loud but deep, mouth-honour, breath,
> Which the poor heart would fain deny, and dare not.

a Explore how Shakespeare presents Macbeth's thoughts and feelings in this extract.
Refer closely to the extract in your answer. **(20 marks)**

b This extract shows Macbeth talking about fear.
Explain the importance of fear elsewhere in the play.
In your answer you must consider:
- how fear is shown
- how fear affects those who experience it.
You should refer to the context of the play in your answer. **(20 marks)**

Unit 8 Write 🖉 your response to the **second part** of this question.

Answers

Unit 1

Page 3

(1) Macbeth, Lady Macbeth, Banquo, Lady Macduff, Boy (son of Macduff), Duncan, Duncan's guards, Young Siward

(2) Twice

(3) (a) Three witches appear on stage. This is followed by news of Scotland's victory in battle against the invading Norwegian army.

(b) Macduff kills Macbeth and Malcolm is made King of Scotland.

(c) Duncan's army repels the invading Norwegian army.

Macbeth and Banquo meet the witches.

Macbeth kills King Duncan.

Macbeth kills Duncan's guards.

Macbeth has Banquo murdered.

Macbeth visits the witches.

Macbeth has Lady Macduff and her son murdered.

Lady Macbeth dies.

Macbeth kills Young Siward.

Macduff kills Macbeth. Malcolm is King of Scotland.

Page 4

(1) (a) **Causes**: Macbeth hears the witches' predictions; Macbeth is made Thane of Cawdor (prompting him to believe the witches' predictions); Lady Macbeth persuades Macbeth to kill King Duncan.

(b) **Consequences**: Macbeth is King of Scotland; Macbeth has Banquo murdered; Macduff kills Macbeth.

Page 5

(1) Arguably, Macbeth would be made Thane of Cawdor; Duncan would remain as King, and be succeeded by Malcolm on his (natural) death.

(2) (b) Possible answers include:

- Macbeth is made Thane of Cawdor: Macbeth might have dismissed the witches' predictions and not acted upon them.

- Lady Macbeth persuades Macbeth: Macbeth might have been tempted, but ultimately have decided not, to kill Duncan.

- Macbeth murders King Duncan: the plot might have then focused more closely on Macbeth's relationship with his wife as she tried and failed to persuade him to kill Duncan.

- Macbeth has Macduff's wife and children murdered: Macduff might not have agreed to, and led, the fight against Macbeth.

Page 6

This student has effectively placed the extract in the context of the whole play, considered its impact, and used this to come to a conclusion: Shakespeare presents Macbeth as clearly influenced by the witches' predictions, either in affirming his ambitions, or showing his belief in the supernatural. The student has selected relevant evidence and focused on the implications of the characters' lines and of Shakespeare's language choices.

Page 7

(a) 1.3; 3.4; 4.1

(b) Arguably, 1.3 and 4.1 (although it is the appearance of Banquo's ghost in 3.4 that drives Macbeth to seek out the witches in 4.1)

(c) 2.2; 3.3; 4.1; 4.2; 5.8

Page 8

Responses could focus on:

- Macbeth's ruthless use of violence in murdering Duncan, Banquo, and Macduff's family

- Macbeth's violent death, his decapitated head displayed on stage at the end of the play.

Unit 2

Page 11

(1) (a) 1, 2 and 4 are arguably the most relevant in commenting on Duncan as a leader. However, 6 could also be used to comment on Duncan's naivety or poor judgement of character. He is replacing the traitor Cawdor, whom he once trusted, with another potential traitor, Macbeth.

(b) 1: Macbeth clearly respects Duncan and, perhaps, feels the need to clearly show this. It could suggest that Duncan responds to this flattery.

2: It suggests that Duncan rewards those who show respect and loyalty.

4: It shows that Duncan is emotional and affectionate, being moved to tears by his army's victory in battle and the loyalty of his subjects. It could be argued that Duncan is unwise to choose this moment to name his own son as his heir, although he does promise more 'nobleness' to 'all deservers'.

Page 12

(1) (a) Duncan has rewarded Macbeth for his loyalty and will reward him again. Duncan shows his gratitude to Banquo as well.

(b) Duncan is, perhaps, demonstrating that those who are loyal will be rewarded. The implication is that Duncan wants his men to respect, and be loyal to, his position of power.

(c) Duncan clearly recognises the need to keep his subjects' loyalty, particularly following the execution of the treacherous Thane of Cawdor. This could suggest that an effective leader recognises that, once gained, power must be nurtured and maintained.

(d) For example: 'I have begun to plant thee, and will labour / To make thee full of growing.'; 'Let me infold thee / And hold thee to my heart.'

Page 13

(1) All are valid.

(2) Examples:

B, A, D, C, F, E

F, B, C, D, A, E

(3) For example:

[F] Shakespeare presents Duncan's leadership as positive and caring because he does not take his power, or the people he has power over, for granted.

<u>In the extract</u> [A] Shakespeare presents King Duncan as warm, generous and grateful for Macbeth and Banquo's victory over the Norwegian army.

<u>For example,</u> [C] Duncan tells Macbeth that he will 'labour / To make thee full of growing', suggesting that Duncan will reward Macbeth with more honours and titles if he remains loyal and fights hard for Duncan.

<u>Similarly,</u> [D] Duncan calls Banquo 'Noble' and embraces him: 'Let me infold thee / And hold thee to my heart', suggesting he feels respect and affection for him.

<u>This shows that</u> [B] Duncan uses his power in a positive way, rewarding his people for their help and support.

<u>In this way</u> [E] the role of king is presented almost like the role of a father, caring for his family.

(4) (a) Key point: A

(b) Evidence: C, D

(c) Comment: B

(d) Response: E, F

Page 14

(1) (a) The student has achieved all of the criteria.

(b) C. Key point: *In this extract, King Duncan appears to be a good leader, using his power to reward those who are loyal to him and fight for him.*

D. Evidence: Macbeth has returned victorious from battle, and has been rewarded for his loyalty with the title of Thane of Cawdor. Duncan seems to promise that Macbeth will continue to be rewarded more if he continues to please Duncan: 'I have begun to plant thee, and will labour / To make thee full of growing.'

E: Comment: While this seems to be a perfect picture of a loyal subject and a grateful king, it could be argued that Duncan is bribing Macbeth with the title of Thane of Cawdor to make sure he stays loyal. Furthermore, this extract comes just after Duncan has had the previous Thane of Cawdor executed for treachery.

F: Response: So this part of the play suggests that, in order to be an effective leader, you must repay loyalty, but be cruel and ruthless when your power is challenged.

Page 16

Responses could focus on:

- Macbeth described as 'brave' by the Captain, and 'valiant' by Duncan, suggesting his positive qualities are recognised and respected at this point in the play
- Macbeth's violent and ruthless attack on Macdonwald described in graphic detail: his sword 'smoked with bloody execution'; 'unseam'd him... fix'd his head upon our battlements...'

Unit 3

Page 19

(1) (a) Examples could include: 'Great', 'worthy', 'Greater'

(b) This could suggest that Lady Macbeth is impressed by, and admires, her husband's achievements, and/or believes that she is able to influence and manipulate his actions both through flattery and by highlighting the inevitable course of events that the witches predicted.

(2) A:

(a) (i) Look innocent; be ruthless.

(ii) She fears her husband's appearance will reveal his plans; to encourage his resolve.

(b)/(c) Imperatives 'Look', 'be' suggest her dominance and control; 'flower', 'serpent' suggest her reliance on deceit and ruthlessness.

B:

(a) (i) Look innocent and I will take care of everything else.

(ii) To calm his fears; to assert her dominance.

(b)/(c) Imperatives 'Look', 'leave' suggest her dominance and control; the euphemism 'the rest', referring to the regicide she plans, suggests her manipulation of Macbeth's thoughts and feelings.

Page 20

(1) (a) All are valid.

(b) Short lines, delivered at speed, might contribute to these moods.

(2) (a) Macbeth says much less than Lady Macbeth; Lady Macbeth does most of the talking.

(b) Macbeth is, perhaps, anxious; Lady Macbeth's excitement and insistence dominate the scene and her husband.

Page 21

(1) All are valid.

(2) The imperatives 'Look' and 'be' begin these abrupt commands, suggesting Lady Macbeth's emphatic dominance of her husband; the contrast of 'flower' and 'serpent' in these abrupt commands emphasises the deceit that her ambitions demand of him.

Page 22

key point focusing on the key words in the question	As soon as Macbeth appears at the start of the extract, Lady Macbeth ruthlessly dominates the scene and tries to influence him.
evidence from the text to support your point	She welcomes him home, calling him 'Great Glamis! worthy Cawdor!'
comments on the evidence and its impact	These short, emphatic exclamations suggest her excitement and are meant to flatter Macbeth. She uses the positive adjectives 'great' and 'worthy' to boost his confidence and make him feel important. She also uses his new title of 'Cawdor' to remind him of the witches' prediction that has already come true, and the rest of the prediction which she wants him to make come true.

a response to the question.	Lady Macbeth doubts her husband will be ruthless enough to do this, and so feels she must flatter and manipulate him to be as ruthless and ambitious as she is.
a comment on language choice(s)	She uses the positive adjectives 'great' and 'worthy' to boost his confidence and make him feel important. She also uses his new title of 'Cawdor' to remind him of the witches' prediction that has already come true, and the rest of the prediction which she wants him to make come true.
a comment on structural choice(s)	These short, emphatic exclamations suggest her excitement and are meant to flatter Macbeth.

Page 24

Responses could focus on:

- Banquo clearly suspects Macbeth but does not plan to challenge him: like Macbeth, he will wait to see if the witches' predictions come true.

- Despite his fears, Banquo expresses his loyalty to Macbeth ('let your Highness command upon me'), suggesting his dishonesty or, perhaps, fear.

Unit 4

Page 27

1. brave, dishonest, ambitious, superstitious, frightened
2. For example: ruthless, unstable, unemotional, unpredictable
3. All responses are arguable; each key scene marks a step in the hardening of Macbeth to the demands of his ruthless ambition.

Page 28

1. a ...in Act 1 Scene 5, she calls upon 'spirits' to 'fill' her with 'direst cruelty'.

   ...in Act 5 Scene 1, she sleepwalks, clearly troubled by guilt.

   ...we are told that she has died, it is suggested 'by self and violent hands' (5.8).

   b Despite her initial, apparently ruthless ambition, Lady Macbeth is increasingly troubled, and ultimately consumed, by guilt.

2. a The extract is from Act 1 Scene 7.

   b Lady Macbeth is presented as ruthless and evil calling upon 'spirits' to fill her with 'direst cruelty'.

   c Her dismissal of guilt in Act 2 Scene 2.

   d All subsequent appearances suggest that she is not as able to ignore or suppress her guilt as she first appears.

   e Her call to be filled with 'direst cruelty' was unsuccessful. She is, arguably, ultimately more susceptible to guilt and remorse than her husband.

Page 29

1. C. He could be saying it because he is a good man. Or it could be because he is not as ruthlessly ambitious as his wife and/or wants to preserve his reputation.

   D. Is it because she wants to show how ruthless and cruel she is? Or because she wants to persuade her husband to be ruthless and cruel?

   E. He could be saying it because he does not want to kill Duncan. Or because he is more worried about failure, and its consequences, than about the murder itself.

2. It could be argued that Macbeth is attempting to reject his wife's manipulations because he is a good man, or because he is more concerned about his reputation and the consequences of failure.

   It could be argued that Lady Macbeth is entirely evil, ruthlessly pursuing her own interests, or that she is supporting her husband in persuading him to achieve his ambitions.

Page 30

1. extract:

   'In some ways, Macbeth is presented as a good man at this point in the play. Although he is ambitious to be king, he is reluctant to murder Duncan in order to achieve that ambition. He firmly tells his wife that "We will proceed no further in this busines", the phrase "we will" suggesting that he is trying to be dominant and reject his wife's demands.'

   'The presentation of Lady Macbeth in this extract also makes Macbeth appear a better man than he really is. She is shown to be controlling, manipulative and ruthless, telling her husband that she will "account his love" according to whether he will kill Duncan.'

2. other parts:

   'Her call for "direst cruelty" and Duncan's "golden opinions" of Macbeth, both of which have been clearly shown earlier in the play, could create the impression that Macbeth is a good man who is being manipulated by his evil wife.'

3. different responses:

   'However, the reasons he gives suggest that perhaps he is not as good as he appears. He tells his wife that he has been "honour'd" by Duncan and has "bought / Golden opinions from all sorts of people". The word "golden" suggests how high these opinions are, and how much he values them, which suggests that he is more worried about his reputation as a good man than actually acting like one.'

Page 32

Responses could focus on:

- Lady Macbeth expresses her anxieties to herself ('our desire is got without content'), then accuses Macbeth of similar anxiety ('thoughts which should indeed have died') and advises Macbeth to be 'bright and jovial'. Perhaps this suggests she is concerned by his mood and the possible consequences of his behaviour.

- Lady Macbeth appears impatient with Macbeth's worries and plans: 'You must leave this.'

- Macbeth clearly expresses his anxiety that they have not 'kill'd' the 'snake' and that his mind is 'full of scorpions'.

Unit 5

Page 35

(1) For example:

Power: 1.4: Duncan shows his power; Macbeth considers what he must do to acquire it.

Ambition: 1.5: Lady Macbeth expresses her ambitions, and fears that Macbeth does not have the ruthlessness needed to achieve them.

Violence: 2.2: the aftermath of the murder of Duncan.

The supernatural: 3.4: the ghost of Banquo appears to Macbeth.

Loyalty: 1.4: the Thane of Cawdor is hanged for treachery; Macbeth is rewarded for his loyalty while secretly planning treachery.

(2) violence/power/ambition – Macbeth has murdered the king in order to further his ambition.

loyalty – Macbeth has ignored any loyalty he owed to the king.

guilt – Macbeth is overcome with guilt, while Lady Macbeth dismisses it.

good and evil – Macbeth's guilt, and Lady Macbeth's denial of it, suggest that Lady Macbeth finds it easier to turn to evil than her husband.

(3) All are valid.

Page 36

(1) A = c; B = a, b, d; C = a, b, d; D = b, c, d

(2) (a) Lady Macbeth suggests that guilt can be avoided by simply not thinking about 'these deeds'. She fears that the guilt will lead to madness. Macbeth fears that his guilt will stop him from ever sleeping again.

(b) The reactions of both characters suggest the power of guilt to dominate, or even damage, the mind.

Page 37

(1) For example: necessary, a great responsibility, corrupting and dangerous.

(2) (a/b) For example:

1.3 and 4.1: Macbeth meets the witches; these dramatic and engaging scenes suggest how the malevolent influence of the supernatural can mislead human beings to make ill-judged decisions with tragic consequences.

3.4: Macbeth sees Banquo's ghost; this dramatic and engaging scene suggests that men can be haunted by their crimes, or by the guilt of their crimes.

(c) The supernatural is essential to the development of the plot and a key element of the play's drama. It is presented as dangerous, destructive and terrifying.

Page 38

(1) The student refers to:
- 3.3: the murder of Banquo
- 3.4: the appearance of Banquo's ghost
- 4.2: the murder of Macduff's family
- Act 5: Macbeth following the murder of Macduff's family.

(2) 'Because he uses murderers to kill Banquo, Shakespeare suggests that Macbeth is trying to avoid the guilt he felt at the murder of Duncan. However, Shakespeare develops Macbeth's guilt, showing it in the form of Banquo's ghost. This suggests that Macbeth is literally being haunted by his feelings of guilt and is terrified of them. It is this guilt that helps the audience to have some sympathy for Macbeth as it shows that he is not completely inhuman and evil.'

'It seems that Macbeth is 'in blood stepped in so far' and so worried and obsessed with his life and his power falling apart, that he has lost his own feelings of guilt, suggesting that by the end of the play Shakespeare wants the audience to see him as either mad or evil.'

(3) 'In the first half of the play he shows guilt at the murders of Duncan and Banquo.' 'However, in the second half of the play, Macbeth shows little guilt or remorse.'

Page 40

Responses could focus on:

- the false appearance Macbeth and Lady Macbeth give to Duncan when they welcome him to their castle, knowing they will murder him
- Lady Macbeth's false appearance of cold cruelty, which soon falters and, eventually, destroys her
- the false appearance of the witches' predictions, promising greatness and invincibility, but bringing Macbeth's destruction.

Unit 6

Page 43

(1) (a) Macbeth appears out of control, reacting to the appearance of Banquo's ghost and oblivious to the other people around him. Lady Macbeth takes control, making excuses for her husband in an attempt to maintain his dignity and authority.

(b) For example: Lady Macbeth appears to be in control of the situation, while Macbeth's desire for power has resulted in his loss of self-control.

(2) (a/b) All are arguably valid. 1.3, 4.1, 1.5, 1.7, 2.2 and 5.8 all suggest Macbeth's lack or loss of control; 3.2 and 4.2 show his attempts to take control.

Page 44

(1) (a) All are arguably valid.

(b) For example:

1.3, 4.1: B, C, D

1.4: E

1.5, 1.7: B, D

2.2: A, B, D

3.2: A, C, D, E

4.2: A, C, D, E

5.1: A, D

5.8: A, D, E

(2) Key points are likely to focus on: Lady Macbeth's and the witches' control over Macbeth; Macbeth's desire for power and his attempts to keep it; the impact of the desire for power on Macbeth and Lady Macbeth.

Page 45

1. A, B, C, D
2. a. For example: D, B, A, C, i.e. focusing first on Lady Macbeth, then on Macbeth.
   b. For example: B, A, C, D, i.e. focusing on the power to control and influence others, then the loss of self-control as a consequence of the desire for power.

Page 46

1. B
2. C

Page 48

Responses could focus on:

- the battle described in Act 1 Scene 2 when Macbeth 'unseam'd' Macdonwald
- the murder of Duncan in Act 2 Scene 2
- the murders of Banquo and Macduff's family
- the development of Macbeth's attitude to murder, moving from crippling guilt to cold acceptance of it as a necessity
- the death of Macbeth.

Unit 7

Page 51

1. This moment in the play shows that Macbeth is easily influenced by the witches, still feeling guilty about the murders of Duncan and Banquo but ruthless in his determination to hold on to power.

   The themes of the supernatural, guilt, power and deception are all relevant to this moment.

2. a. 3.1: Banquo, Macbeth; 3.2: Macbeth, Lady Macbeth; 4.2: Macbeth; 4.3: Macduff
   b. Arguably almost all explore one or more key themes. For example: 3.1: ambition, power, violence; 3.2: guilt/remorse, ambition; 3.3: violence; 3.4 & 3.5: the supernatural; 4.2: violence; 4.3: violence, revenge
   c. 3.1, 3.3, 4.2
   d. 3.1–3.4, 4.2, 4.3

Page 52

1. For example: The witches' predictions have a significant influence on Macbeth.
2. A, B, D, E, F and H are all relevant.
3. a. Aa, Ab, Bb, Da and Dc are all relevant.
   b. For example: The witches' predictions have a significant influence on Macbeth's decision to murder Duncan.

Page 53

1. All are valid.
2. For example:

   Macbeth has Macduff's family murdered in response to the witches' predictions in Act 4 Scene 1.

   This suggests Macbeth's ruthless desire to maintain his power and his reliance on the witches' predictions rather than his own judgement.

It emphasises the central role that the witches' predictions have in the development of the play.

This murder of a woman and child is intended to shock and repulse the audience, destroying any remaining sympathy for Macbeth.

Page 54

uses a key event as evidence	Another consequence of the witches' predictions at the start of the play is Macbeth's decision to have Banquo murdered.
explains the context of the evidence	The witches predicted that Banquo's descendants would become kings of Scotland and so Macbeth fears that Banquo and his son Fleance will challenge his power.
analysis comments on character	This shows the influence of the witches' predictions on Macbeth's choices and decisions but also his heartless ruthlessness in acting on them. Banquo is Macbeth's friend and they fought together in the battle at the start of the play.
analysis comments on theme	the witches' predictions are influencing Macbeth to put power above friendship and loyalty.
analysis comments on Shakespeare's intention	This makes his murder even more shocking for the audience.

Page 56

Responses could focus on:

- the battle described in Act 1 Scene 2 when Macbeth 'unseam'd' Macdonwald
- the murder of Duncan in Act 2 Scene 2
- the murders of Banquo and Macduff's family
- the development of Macbeth's attitude to murder, moving from crippling guilt to cold acceptance of it as a necessity
- the death of Macbeth.

Unit 8

Page 59

1. All are relevant, apart from James I's publication A Counterblaste to Tobacco.
2. The witches: 17th century attitudes to witchcraft

   Lady Macbeth: 17th century attitudes to women and witchcraft

   Macbeth/Murder of Duncan: The divine right of kings

Page 60

1. a. identifies the time in which the play was written: B, C

   identifies a relevant belief, attitude or situation at the time: A, B, C

   considers Shakespeare's intention: B

   considers the impact on an audience: B, C

   compares today's audience with Shakespeare's audience: C

(b) B and C are the most detailed, developed comments on context.

(2) (a) Responses are likely to focus on the dramatic impact of this opening scene being heightened by a contemporary audience's fear of witchcraft.

Page 61

(1) (a) Sentences A–D focus on impact; Sentences a–d focus on context.

(b) b is relevant to A and B; a and d are relevant to C and D; c is arguably linked to D but very tenuously.

Page 62

uses a key event as evidence	When Lady Macbeth reads Macbeth's letter about the witches' predictions, she calls on the forces of evil
uses a quotation as evidence	to 'unsex' her and fill her with 'direst cruelty' so that she has the power to persuade her husband to murder Duncan.
comments on the impact of the evidence	This is a disturbing moment in the play for a modern audience as it suggests she is trying to overcome her conscience so that she can persuade Macbeth to commit murder.
identifies a relevant contextual point	However, because Shakespeare's audience firmly believed in 'spirits' and witches and the harm that they could do to normal human beings,
explores Shakespeare's intention in the light of this contextual point	Shakespeare wants his audience to be both shocked and disturbed by Lady Macbeth and even more so because this is her first appearance in the play.
explores the audience's response in the light of this contextual point	this would be a terrifying moment for them.

Page 64

Responses could focus on:

- Macbeth's fear at the prospect of murdering Duncan: his doubts in Act 1, his hallucination of a dagger in Act 2
- Macbeth's fear and guilt following the murder of Duncan in Act 2 Scene 2
- Macbeth's fear of Banquo and Macduff, resulting in their murders
- Macbeth's fear at the appearance of Banquo's ghost, driving him to visit the witches.

Unit 9

Page 67

(1) For example:

Macbeth: brave, ambitious, ruthless, disturbed, submissive

Lady Macbeth: ambitious, ruthless, decisive, disturbed, duplicitous, delusional

(2) For example:

Macbeth: tension, concern, disappointment, revulsion, shock, sympathy

Lady Macbeth: tension, concern, revulsion, shock, sympathy

Page 68

(1) (a) When, whereas, because

(b) All version 'B's use conjunctions to express the relationship between the two clauses more clearly.

(2) For example:

When Lady Macbeth receives a letter from Macbeth, she calls upon 'spirits' to fill her with cruelty.

Although Lady Macbeth is manipulative, Macbeth makes the decision to murder Duncan.

Macbeth feels guilt at the murder of Duncan but he shows none at the killing of Macduff's family.

Page 69

(1) For example:

(a) Macbeth believes the witches' predictions and chooses to act on them.

(b) Macbeth believes the witches' predictions because they confirm his hopes and fears.

(c) Macbeth believes the witches' predictions, which is, perhaps, his poorest decision in the play.

(d) Macbeth believes the witches' predictions, misunderstanding their true meaning.

(2) For example:

(a) Lady Macbeth seems to have total control, which encourages the audience to see Macbeth as powerless.

(b) Macbeth chooses to murder Banquo without Lady Macbeth's influence, creating the impression that he is becoming more independent and more ruthless.

Page 70

(1) (a)/(b) For example: good (loyal, brave, honourable); telling (persuading, encouraging, urging); makes (leads, encourages, forces); weak (impotent, submissive, powerless).

(c)/(d) For example:

At the start of the play Macbeth is presented as loyal and courageous. He fights successfully in battle for King Duncan and is described as 'brave'. When he goes home to Lady Macbeth, she starts persuading him to murder Duncan, which suggests that it is Lady Macbeth who leads her husband to make bad choices and gives the impression that Macbeth is good but impotent.

Notes